CONSTRUCTION
&
MAINTENANCE
DAILY LOG

Copyright © 2018

ISBN-10: 0-9766588-4-4

ISBN-13: 978- 0-9766588-4-9

Printed in the United States of America

SAFETY SAVES
/// LIVES
TIME - MONEY

Name: _____

Address:

    Street _____

    City _____ State _____ Zip _____

Company:

    Name _____

    Street _____

    City _____ State _____ Zip _____

Telephone:

    Home ( ) _____

    Office ( ) _____

    Fax ( ) _____

    Mobile ( ) _____

    Pager ( ) _____

Notes: _____

_____

_____

_____

_____

In an emergency, please notify:

    Name _____

    Street _____

    City _____ State _____ Zip _____

    Telephone ( ) _____

TELEPHONE NUMBERS

NAME	AREA CODE	PHONE

TELEPHONE NUMBERS

NAME	AREA CODE	PHONE

TELEPHONE NUMBERS

NAME	AREA CODE	PHONE

TELEPHONE NUMBERS

NAME	AREA CODE	PHONE

MATERIAL & EQUIPMENT PURCHASE RECORD

DATE	INVOICE NO.	SUPPLIER	DESCRIPTION	PRICE

MATERIAL & EQUIPMENT PURCHASE RECORD

DATE	INVOICE NO.	SUPPLIER	DESCRIPTION	PRICE

MATERIAL & EQUIPMENT PURCHASE RECORD

DATE	INVOICE NO.	SUPPLIER	DESCRIPTION	PRICE

MATERIAL & EQUIPMENT PURCHASE RECORD

DATE	INVOICE NO.	SUPPLIER	DESCRIPTION	PRICE

MATERIAL & EQUIPMENT PURCHASE RECORD

DATE	INVOICE NO.	SUPPLIER	DESCRIPTION	PRICE

MATERIAL & EQUIPMENT PURCHASE RECORD

DATE	INVOICE NO.	SUPPLIER	DESCRIPTION	PRICE

MATERIAL & EQUIPMENT PURCHASE RECORD

DATE	INVOICE NO.	SUPPLIER	DESCRIPTION	PRICE

MATERIAL & EQUIPMENT PURCHASE RECORD

DATE	INVOICE NO.	SUPPLIER	DESCRIPTION	PRICE

MATERIAL & EQUIPMENT PURCHASE RECORD

DATE	INVOICE NO.	SUPPLIER	DESCRIPTION	PRICE

MATERIAL & EQUIPMENT PURCHASE RECORD

DATE	INVOICE NO.	SUPPLIER	DESCRIPTION	PRICE

DAY _____   DAILY LOG   20___ JAN. 1

CONTRACTOR _____ JOB NAME _____ JOB NO _____

Work Performed Today _____	Weather _____
_____	Temp. AM _____PM _____
_____	
_____	Safety Meeting _____
_____	

Work Force   **No.**

Superintendent _____
Clerk _____
Bricklayers _____
Carpenters _____
Cement Masons _____
Electricians _____
Iron Workers _____
Laborers _____
Operating Eng. _____
Plumbers _____
Pipe Fitters _____
Sheet Metal _____
Truck Drivers _____

Problems - Delays _____

Total _____

Sub-Contractor Progress _____

Equipment	Hrs.

Special Assignments _____

Extra Work	Authorized By	Approx. Price

Equipment Rented Today	Rented From	Rate

Material Purchased

Supervisor's Signature _____

2 JAN. 20___   DAILY LOG   DAY _____

CONTRACTOR _____ JOB NAME _____ JOB NO._____

Work Performed Today _____

_____

_____

_____

_____

_____

_____

_____

_____

_____

_____

_____

_____

Problems - Delays _____

_____

_____

_____

Sub-Contractor Progress _____

_____

_____

_____

Special Assignments _____

_____

_____

| Weather | _____ |
| Temp. AM _____ PM _____ |
| Safety Meeting _____ |

Work Force	No.
Superintendent	_____
Clerk	_____
Bricklayers	_____
Carpenters	_____
Cement Masons	_____
Electricians	_____
Iron Workers	_____
Laborers	_____
Operating Eng.	_____
Plumbers	_____
Pipe Fitters	_____
Sheet Metal	_____
Truck Drivers	_____
Total	_____

Equipment	Hrs.

Material Purchased

Extra Work	Authorized By	Approx. Price

Equipment Rented Today	Rented From	Rate

Supervisor's Signature _____

DAY _____   DAILY LOG   20___ JAN. 3

CONTRACTOR _____ JOB NAME _____ JOB NO _____

Work Performed Today _____

_____

_____

_____

_____

_____

_____

_____

_____

_____

_____

_____

_____

_____

Problems - Delays _____

_____

_____

_____

Sub-Contractor Progress _____

_____

_____

Special Assignments _____

_____

_____

| Weather _____ |
| Temp. AM _____ PM _____ |
| Safety Meeting _____ |

Work Force	No.
Superintendent	_____
Clerk	_____
Bricklayers	_____
Carpenters	_____
Cement Masons	_____
Electricians	_____
Iron Workers	_____
Laborers	_____
Operating Eng.	_____
Plumbers	_____
Pipe Fitters	_____
Sheet Metal	_____
Truck Drivers	_____
Total	_____

Equipment	Hrs.

Material Purchased	

Extra Work	Authorized By	Approx. Price

Equipment Rented Today	Rented From	Rate

Supervisor's Signature _____

4 JAN. 20___   DAILY LOG   DAY _____

CONTRACTOR _____ JOB NAME _____ JOB NO._____

Work Performed Today _____

_____

_____

_____

_____

_____

_____

_____

_____

_____

_____

_____

_____

Problems - Delays _____

_____

_____

_____

Sub-Contractor Progress _____

_____

_____

_____

Special Assignments _____

_____

_____

| Weather _____ |
| Temp. AM _____ PM _____ |
| Safety Meeting _____ |

Work Force	No.
Superintendent	_____
Clerk	_____
Bricklayers	_____
Carpenters	_____
Cement Masons	_____
Electricians	_____
Iron Workers	_____
Laborers	_____
Operating Eng.	_____
Plumbers	_____
Pipe Fitters	_____
Sheet Metal	_____
Truck Drivers	_____
Total	_____

Equipment	Hrs.

Extra Work	Authorized By	Approx. Price

Equipment Rented Today	Rented From	Rate

Material Purchased

Supervisor's Signature _____

DAY _____   DAILY LOG   20___ JAN. 5

CONTRACTOR _____ JOB NAME _____ JOB NO _____

Work Performed Today _____

_____

_____

_____

_____

_____

_____

_____

_____

_____

_____

_____

_____

_____

Problems - Delays _____

_____

_____

_____

Sub-Contractor Progress _____

_____

_____

_____

Special Assignments _____

_____

_____

_____

Extra Work	Authorized By	Approx. Price

Equipment Rented Today	Rented From	Rate

Supervisor's Signature _____

Weather _____

Temp. AM _____ PM _____

Safety Meeting _____

Work Force	No.
Superintendent	_____
Clerk	_____
Bricklayers	_____
Carpenters	_____
Cement Masons	_____
Electricians	_____
Iron Workers	_____
Laborers	_____
Operating Eng.	_____
Plumbers	_____
Pipe Fitters	_____
Sheet Metal	_____
Truck Drivers	_____
Total	_____

Equipment	Hrs.

Material Purchased

6 JAN. 20___   DAILY LOG   DAY _____

CONTRACTOR _____ JOB NAME _____ JOB NO. _____

Work Performed Today _____	Weather _____
	Temp. AM _____ PM _____
	Safety Meeting _____

Work Force	No.
Superintendent	_____
Clerk	_____
Bricklayers	_____
Carpenters	_____
Cement Masons	_____
Electricians	_____
Iron Workers	_____
Laborers	_____
Operating Eng.	_____
Plumbers	_____
Pipe Fitters	_____
Sheet Metal	_____
Truck Drivers	_____
Total	_____

Problems - Delays _____

Sub-Contractor Progress _____

Equipment	Hrs.

Special Assignments _____

Extra Work	Authorized By	Approx. Price

Equipment Rented Today	Rented From	Rate

Material Purchased

Supervisor's Signature _____

DAY _____   DAILY LOG   20___ JAN. 7

CONTRACTOR _____ JOB NAME _____ JOB NO _____

Work Performed Today _____	Weather _____
_____	Temp. AM _____ PM _____
_____	Safety Meeting _____

Work Force	No.
Superintendent	_____
Clerk	_____
Bricklayers	_____
Carpenters	_____
Cement Masons	_____
Electricians	_____
Iron Workers	_____
Laborers	_____
Operating Eng.	_____
Plumbers	_____
Pipe Fitters	_____
Sheet Metal	_____
Truck Drivers	_____
Total	_____

Problems - Delays _____

Sub-Contractor Progress _____

Equipment	Hrs.

Special Assignments _____

Extra Work	Authorized By	Approx. Price

Equipment Rented Today	Rented From	Rate

Material Purchased

Supervisor's Signature _____

8 JAN. 20___   DAILY LOG   DAY _____

CONTRACTOR _____ JOB NAME _____ JOB NO. _____

Work Performed Today	Weather _____
	Temp. AM _____ PM _____
	Safety Meeting _____

Work Force	No.
Superintendent	_____
Clerk	_____
Bricklayers	_____
Carpenters	_____
Cement Masons	_____
Electricians	_____
Iron Workers	_____
Laborers	_____
Operating Eng.	_____
Plumbers	_____
Pipe Fitters	_____
Sheet Metal	_____
Truck Drivers	_____
Total	_____

Problems - Delays _____

Equipment	Hrs.

Sub-Contractor Progress _____

Special Assignments _____

Extra Work	Authorized By	Approx. Price

Equipment Rented Today	Rented From	Rate

Material Purchased

Supervisor's Signature _____

DAY _____   DAILY LOG   20___ JAN. 9

CONTRACTOR _____ JOB NAME _____ JOB NO _____

Work Performed Today _____

_____

_____

_____

_____

_____

_____

_____

_____

_____

_____

_____

_____

_____

Problems - Delays _____

_____

_____

_____

Sub-Contractor Progress _____

_____

_____

Special Assignments _____

_____

_____

Extra Work	Authorized By	Approx. Price

Equipment Rented Today	Rented From	Rate

Supervisor's Signature _____

Weather _____

Temp. AM _____ PM _____

Safety Meeting _____

Work Force	No.
Superintendent	_____
Clerk	_____
Bricklayers	_____
Carpenters	_____
Cement Masons	_____
Electricians	_____
Iron Workers	_____
Laborers	_____
Operating Eng.	_____
Plumbers	_____
Pipe Fitters	_____
Sheet Metal	_____
Truck Drivers	_____
Total	_____

Equipment	Hrs.

Material Purchased

10 JAN. 20___   DAILY LOG   DAY _____

CONTRACTOR _____ JOB NAME _____ JOB NO. _____

Work Performed Today _____

_____

_____

_____

_____

_____

_____

_____

_____

_____

_____

_____

_____

Problems - Delays _____

_____

_____

_____

Sub-Contractor Progress _____

_____

_____

_____

Special Assignments _____

_____

_____

Weather	_____
Temp. AM _____ PM _____	
Safety Meeting _____	

Work Force	No.
Superintendent	_____
Clerk	_____
Bricklayers	_____
Carpenters	_____
Cement Masons	_____
Electricians	_____
Iron Workers	_____
Laborers	_____
Operating Eng.	_____
Plumbers	_____
Pipe Fitters	_____
Sheet Metal	_____
Truck Drivers	_____
Total	_____

Equipment	Hrs.

Material Purchased

Extra Work	Authorized By	Approx. Price

Equipment Rented Today	Rented From	Rate

Supervisor's Signature _____

DAY _____   DAILY LOG   20___   JAN. 11

CONTRACTOR _____   JOB NAME _____   JOB NO _____

Work Performed Today _____

_____

_____

_____

_____

_____

_____

_____

_____

_____

_____

_____

_____

Problems - Delays _____

_____

_____

_____

Sub-Contractor Progress _____

_____

_____

Special Assignments _____

_____

_____

| Weather _____ |
| Temp. AM _____ PM _____ |
| Safety Meeting _____ |

Work Force	No.
Superintendent	_____
Clerk	_____
Bricklayers	_____
Carpenters	_____
Cement Masons	_____
Electricians	_____
Iron Workers	_____
Laborers	_____
Operating Eng.	_____
Plumbers	_____
Pipe Fitters	_____
Sheet Metal	_____
Truck Drivers	_____
Total	_____

Equipment	Hrs.

Extra Work	Authorized By	Approx. Price

Equipment Rented Today	Rented From	Rate

Material Purchased

Supervisor's Signature _____

12 JAN. 20___ DAILY LOG DAY _____

CONTRACTOR _____ JOB NAME _____ JOB NO._____

Work Performed Today _____

_____

_____

_____

_____

_____

_____

_____

_____

_____

_____

_____

_____

Problems - Delays _____

_____

_____

_____

Sub-Contractor Progress _____

_____

_____

_____

Special Assignments _____

_____

Weather	_____
Temp. AM _____	PM _____
Safety Meeting	_____

Work Force	No.
Superintendent	_____
Clerk	_____
Bricklayers	_____
Carpenters	_____
Cement Masons	_____
Electricians	_____
Iron Workers	_____
Laborers	_____
Operating Eng.	_____
Plumbers	_____
Pipe Fitters	_____
Sheet Metal	_____
Truck Drivers	_____
Total	_____

Equipment	Hrs.

Extra Work	Authorized By	Approx. Price

Equipment Rented Today	Rented From	Rate

Material Purchased

Supervisor's Signature _____

DAY _____   DAILY LOG   20___ JAN. 13

CONTRACTOR _____ JOB NAME _____ JOB NO _____

Work Performed Today _____	Weather _____
	Temp. AM _____PM _____

Work Performed Today (continued lines)

| | Safety Meeting _____ |

Work Force	No.
Superintendent	_____
Clerk	_____
Bricklayers	_____
Carpenters	_____
Cement Masons	_____
Electricians	_____
Iron Workers	_____
Laborers	_____
Operating Eng.	_____
Plumbers	_____
Pipe Fitters	_____
Sheet Metal	_____
Truck Drivers	_____
Total	_____

Problems - Delays _____

Sub-Contractor Progress _____

Equipment	Hrs.

Special Assignments _____

Extra Work	Authorized By	Approx. Price	Material Purchased

Equipment Rented Today	Rented From	Rate	

Supervisor's Signature _____

14 JAN. 20___   DAILY LOG   DAY _____

CONTRACTOR _____ JOB NAME _____ JOB NO._____

Work Performed Today _____	Weather _____
	Temp. AM _____ PM _____
	Safety Meeting _____

Work Force	No.
Superintendent	_____
Clerk	_____
Bricklayers	_____
Carpenters	_____
Cement Masons	_____
Electricians	_____
Iron Workers	_____
Laborers	_____
Operating Eng.	_____
Plumbers	_____
Pipe Fitters	_____
Sheet Metal	_____
Truck Drivers	_____
Total	_____

Problems - Delays _____

Equipment	Hrs.

Sub-Contractor Progress _____

Special Assignments _____

Material Purchased	

Extra Work	Authorized By	Approx. Price

Equipment Rented Today	Rented From	Rate

Supervisor's Signature _____

DAY _____   DAILY LOG   20___ JAN. 15

CONTRACTOR _____ JOB NAME _____ JOB NO _____

| Work Performed Today _____ | Weather _____ |
| _____ | Temp. AM _____ PM _____ |

Work Performed Today _____

_____

_____

_____

_____

_____

_____

_____

_____

_____

_____

_____

_____

_____

Weather _____

Temp. AM _____ PM _____

Safety Meeting _____

Work Force	No.
Superintendent	_____
Clerk	_____
Bricklayers	_____
Carpenters	_____
Cement Masons	_____
Electricians	_____
Iron Workers	_____
Laborers	_____
Operating Eng.	_____
Plumbers	_____
Pipe Fitters	_____
Sheet Metal	_____
Truck Drivers	_____
Total	_____

Problems - Delays _____

_____

_____

_____

Sub-Contractor Progress _____

_____

_____

_____

Special Assignments _____

_____

_____

Equipment	Hrs.

Extra Work	Authorized By	Approx. Price

Equipment Rented Today	Rented From	Rate

Material Purchased

Material Purchased

Supervisor's Signature _____

16 JAN. 20____　　　　　　DAILY LOG　　　　　　DAY _____

CONTRACTOR _____ JOB NAME _____ JOB NO._____

Work Performed Today _____

_____

_____

Weather _____

Temp. AM _____ PM _____

Safety Meeting _____

Work Force	No.
Superintendent	_____
Clerk	_____
Bricklayers	_____
Carpenters	_____
Cement Masons	_____
Electricians	_____
Iron Workers	_____
Laborers	_____
Operating Eng.	_____
Plumbers	_____
Pipe Fitters	_____
Sheet Metal	_____
Truck Drivers	_____
Total	_____

Problems - Delays _____

_____

Sub-Contractor Progress _____

Equipment	Hrs.

Special Assignments _____

Material Purchased

Extra Work	Authorized By	Approx. Price

Equipment Rented Today	Rented From	Rate

Supervisor's Signature _____

DAY _____   DAILY LOG   20___ JAN. 17

CONTRACTOR _____ JOB NAME _____ JOB NO _____

| Work Performed Today _____ | Weather _____ |
| | Temp. AM _____PM _____ |

Safety Meeting _____

Work Force	No.
Superintendent	_____
Clerk	_____
Bricklayers	_____
Carpenters	_____
Cement Masons	_____
Electricians	_____
Iron Workers	_____
Laborers	_____
Operating Eng.	_____
Plumbers	_____
Pipe Fitters	_____
Sheet Metal	_____
Truck Drivers	_____
Total	_____

Problems - Delays _____

Sub-Contractor Progress _____

Equipment	Hrs.

Special Assignments _____

Extra Work	Authorized By	Approx. Price

Material Purchased	

Equipment Rented Today	Rented From	Rate

Supervisor's Signature _____

18 JAN. 20____   DAILY LOG   DAY _____

CONTRACTOR _____ JOB NAME _____ JOB NO._____

Work Performed Today _____

_____

_____

_____

_____

_____

_____

_____

_____

_____

_____

_____

_____

_____

_____

Problems - Delays _____

_____

_____

_____

Sub-Contractor Progress _____

_____

_____

_____

Special Assignments _____

_____

_____

| Weather _____ |
| Temp. AM _____ PM _____ |

| Safety Meeting _____ |

Work Force	No.
Superintendent	_____
Clerk	_____
Bricklayers	_____
Carpenters	_____
Cement Masons	_____
Electricians	_____
Iron Workers	_____
Laborers	_____
Operating Eng.	_____
Plumbers	_____
Pipe Fitters	_____
Sheet Metal	_____
Truck Drivers	_____
Total	_____

Equipment	Hrs.

Extra Work	Authorized By	Approx. Price

Equipment Rented Today	Rented From	Rate

Material Purchased

Supervisor's Signature _____

DAY _____ DAILY LOG 20___ JAN. 19

CONTRACTOR _____ JOB NAME _____ JOB NO _____

Work Performed Today _____

_____

_____

_____

_____

_____

_____

_____

_____

_____

_____

_____

_____

_____

_____

Problems - Delays _____

_____

_____

_____

Sub-Contractor Progress _____

_____

_____

Special Assignments _____

_____

_____

Extra Work	Authorized By	Approx. Price

Equipment Rented Today	Rented From	Rate

Supervisor's Signature _____

Weather _____

Temp. AM _____PM _____

Safety Meeting _____

Work Force	No.
Superintendent	_____
Clerk	_____
Bricklayers	_____
Carpenters	_____
Cement Masons	_____
Electricians	_____
Iron Workers	_____
Laborers	_____
Operating Eng.	_____
Plumbers	_____
Pipe Fitters	_____
Sheet Metal	_____
Truck Drivers	_____
Total	_____

Equipment	Hrs.

Material Purchased

20 JAN. 20____   DAILY LOG   DAY _____

CONTRACTOR _____ JOB NAME _____ JOB NO._____

Work Performed Today _____

_____

_____

_____

_____

_____

_____

_____

_____

_____

_____

_____

_____

_____

Problems - Delays _____

_____

_____

_____

Sub-Contractor Progress _____

_____

_____

Special Assignments _____

_____

_____

Extra Work	Authorized By	Approx. Price

Equipment Rented Today	Rented From	Rate

Supervisor's Signature _____

Weather _____

Temp. AM _____ PM _____

Safety Meeting _____

Work Force	No.
Superintendent	_____
Clerk	_____
Bricklayers	_____
Carpenters	_____
Cement Masons	_____
Electricians	_____
Iron Workers	_____
Laborers	_____
Operating Eng.	_____
Plumbers	_____
Pipe Fitters	_____
Sheet Metal	_____
Truck Drivers	_____
Total	_____

Equipment	Hrs.

Material Purchased

DAY _____   DAILY LOG   20___ JAN. 21

CONTRACTOR _____ JOB NAME _____ JOB NO _____

Work Performed Today _____	Weather _____
_____	Temp. AM _____PM _____
_____	Safety Meeting _____

Work Force	No.
Superintendent	_____
Clerk	_____
Bricklayers	_____
Carpenters	_____
Cement Masons	_____
Electricians	_____
Iron Workers	_____
Laborers	_____
Operating Eng.	_____
Plumbers	_____
Pipe Fitters	_____
Sheet Metal	_____
Truck Drivers	_____
Total	_____

Problems - Delays _____

Sub-Contractor Progress _____

Equipment	Hrs.

Special Assignments _____

Extra Work	Authorized By	Approx. Price

Equipment Rented Today	Rented From	Rate

Material Purchased

Supervisor's Signature _____

22 JAN. 20___   DAILY LOG   DAY _____

CONTRACTOR _____ JOB NAME _____ JOB NO._____

Work Performed Today	Weather _____

Work Performed Today _____

_____

_____

_____

_____

_____

_____

_____

_____

_____

_____

_____

_____

Problems - Delays _____

_____

_____

_____

Sub-Contractor Progress _____

_____

_____

_____

Special Assignments _____

_____

_____

Weather _____

Temp. AM _____PM _____

Safety Meeting _____

Work Force	No.
Superintendent	_____
Clerk	_____
Bricklayers	_____
Carpenters	_____
Cement Masons	_____
Electricians	_____
Iron Workers	_____
Laborers	_____
Operating Eng.	_____
Plumbers	_____
Pipe Fitters	_____
Sheet Metal	_____
Truck Drivers	_____
Total	_____

Equipment	Hrs.

Extra Work	Authorized By	Approx. Price

Equipment Rented Today	Rented From	Rate

Material Purchased

Supervisor's Signature _____

DAY _____   DAILY LOG   20___   JAN. 23

CONTRACTOR _____ JOB NAME _____ JOB NO _____

Work Performed Today _____	Weather _____
	Temp. AM _____ PM _____
	Safety Meeting _____

Work Force	No.
Superintendent	_____
Clerk	_____
Bricklayers	_____
Carpenters	_____
Cement Masons	_____
Electricians	_____
Iron Workers	_____
Laborers	_____
Operating Eng.	_____
Plumbers	_____
Pipe Fitters	_____
Sheet Metal	_____
Truck Drivers	_____
Total	_____

Problems - Delays _____

Equipment	Hrs.

Sub-Contractor Progress _____

Special Assignments _____

Material Purchased

Extra Work	Authorized By	Approx. Price

Equipment Rented Today	Rented From	Rate

Supervisor's Signature _____

24 JAN. 20___   DAILY LOG   DAY _____

CONTRACTOR _____ JOB NAME _____ JOB NO._____

Work Performed Today _____

_____

_____

_____

_____

_____

_____

_____

_____

_____

_____

_____

_____

_____

Problems - Delays _____

_____

_____

_____

Sub-Contractor Progress _____

_____

_____

Special Assignments _____

_____

_____

Weather	_____
Temp. AM _____ PM _____	
Safety Meeting _____	

Work Force	No.
Superintendent	_____
Clerk	_____
Bricklayers	_____
Carpenters	_____
Cement Masons	_____
Electricians	_____
Iron Workers	_____
Laborers	_____
Operating Eng.	_____
Plumbers	_____
Pipe Fitters	_____
Sheet Metal	_____
Truck Drivers	_____
Total	_____

Equipment	Hrs.

Extra Work	Authorized By	Approx. Price

Equipment Rented Today	Rented From	Rate

Material Purchased

Supervisor's Signature _____

DAY _____   DAILY LOG   20___ JAN. 25

CONTRACTOR _____ JOB NAME _____ JOB NO _____

Work Performed Today _____

_____

_____

_____

_____

_____

_____

_____

_____

_____

_____

_____

_____

_____

Problems - Delays _____

_____

_____

_____

Sub-Contractor Progress _____

_____

_____

_____

Special Assignments _____

_____

_____

_____

Extra Work	Authorized By	Approx. Price

Equipment Rented Today	Rented From	Rate

Supervisor's Signature _____

Weather _____

Temp. AM _____PM _____

Safety Meeting _____

Work Force	No.
Superintendent	_____
Clerk	_____
Bricklayers	_____
Carpenters	_____
Cement Masons	_____
Electricians	_____
Iron Workers	_____
Laborers	_____
Operating Eng.	_____
Plumbers	_____
Pipe Fitters	_____
Sheet Metal	_____
Truck Drivers	_____
Total	_____

Equipment	Hrs.

Material Purchased

26 JAN. 20___   DAILY LOG   DAY _____

CONTRACTOR _____ JOB NAME _____ JOB NO._____

Work Performed Today _____

_____

_____

_____

_____

_____

_____

_____

_____

_____

_____

_____

_____

Problems - Delays _____

_____

_____

_____

Sub-Contractor Progress _____

_____

_____

_____

Special Assignments _____

_____

_____

Weather _____

Temp. AM _____PM _____

Safety Meeting _____

Work Force	No.
Superintendent	_____
Clerk	_____
Bricklayers	_____
Carpenters	_____
Cement Masons	_____
Electricians	_____
Iron Workers	_____
Laborers	_____
Operating Eng.	_____
Plumbers	_____
Pipe Fitters	_____
Sheet Metal	_____
Truck Drivers	_____
Total	_____

Equipment	Hrs.

Extra Work	Authorized By	Approx. Price

Equipment Rented Today	Rented From	Rate

Material Purchased

Supervisor's Signature _____

DAY _____   DAILY LOG   20___ JAN. 27

CONTRACTOR _____ JOB NAME _____ JOB NO _____

Work Performed Today _____

_____

_____

_____

_____

_____

_____

_____

_____

_____

_____

_____

_____

_____

_____

Problems - Delays _____

_____

_____

_____

Sub-Contractor Progress _____

_____

_____

_____

Special Assignments _____

_____

_____

_____

Extra Work	Authorized By	Approx. Price

Equipment Rented Today	Rented From	Rate

Supervisor's Signature _____

Weather _____

Temp. AM _____ PM _____

Safety Meeting _____

Work Force	No.
Superintendent	_____
Clerk	_____
Bricklayers	_____
Carpenters	_____
Cement Masons	_____
Electricians	_____
Iron Workers	_____
Laborers	_____
Operating Eng.	_____
Plumbers	_____
Pipe Fitters	_____
Sheet Metal	_____
Truck Drivers	_____
Total	_____

Equipment	Hrs.

Material Purchased

28 JAN. 20___   DAILY LOG   DAY _____

CONTRACTOR _____ JOB NAME _____ JOB NO. _____

Work Performed Today _____	Weather _____
	Temp. AM _____ PM _____
_____	
_____	Safety Meeting _____
_____	

Work Force	No.
Superintendent	_____
Clerk	_____
Bricklayers	_____
Carpenters	_____
Cement Masons	_____
Electricians	_____
Iron Workers	_____
Laborers	_____
Operating Eng.	_____
Plumbers	_____
Pipe Fitters	_____
Sheet Metal	_____
Truck Drivers	_____
Total	_____

Problems - Delays _____
_____
_____
_____

Sub-Contractor Progress _____
_____
_____
_____

Equipment	Hrs.

Special Assignments _____
_____
_____

Extra Work	Authorized By	Approx. Price

Equipment Rented Today	Rented From	Rate

Material Purchased

Supervisor's Signature _____

DAY _____   DAILY LOG   20____ JAN. 29

CONTRACTOR _____ JOB NAME _____ JOB NO _____

Work Performed Today _____	Weather _____
_____	Temp. AM _____ PM _____
_____	Safety Meeting _____

Work Force	No.
Superintendent	_____
Clerk	_____
Bricklayers	_____
Carpenters	_____
Cement Masons	_____
Electricians	_____
Iron Workers	_____
Laborers	_____
Operating Eng.	_____
Plumbers	_____
Pipe Fitters	_____
Sheet Metal	_____
Truck Drivers	_____
Total	_____

Problems - Delays _____

Equipment	Hrs.

Sub-Contractor Progress _____

Special Assignments _____

Material Purchased

Extra Work	Authorized By	Approx. Price

Equipment Rented Today	Rented From	Rate

Supervisor's Signature _____

30 JAN. 20___　　　　　　DAILY LOG　　　　　DAY _____

CONTRACTOR _____ JOB NAME _____ JOB NO._____

Work Performed Today _____

_____

_____

_____

_____

_____

_____

_____

_____

_____

_____

_____

Problems - Delays _____

_____

_____

_____

Sub-Contractor Progress _____

_____

_____

_____

Special Assignments _____

_____

_____

Weather	
Temp. AM _____ PM _____	
Safety Meeting _____	

Work Force	No.
Superintendent	_____
Clerk	_____
Bricklayers	_____
Carpenters	_____
Cement Masons	_____
Electricians	_____
Iron Workers	_____
Laborers	_____
Operating Eng.	_____
Plumbers	_____
Pipe Fitters	_____
Sheet Metal	_____
Truck Drivers	_____
Total	_____

Equipment	Hrs.

Extra Work	Authorized By	Approx. Price

Equipment Rented Today	Rented From	Rate

Material Purchased

Supervisor's Signature _____

DAY _____   DAILY LOG   20___ JAN. 31

CONTRACTOR _____ JOB NAME _____ JOB NO _____

Work Performed Today _____

_____

_____

_____

_____

_____

_____

_____

_____

_____

_____

_____

_____

_____

Problems - Delays _____

_____

_____

_____

Sub-Contractor Progress _____

_____

_____

_____

Special Assignments _____

_____

_____

Extra Work	Authorized By	Approx. Price

Equipment Rented Today	Rented From	Rate

Supervisor's Signature _____

Weather _____

Temp. AM _____PM _____

Safety Meeting _____

Work Force	No.
Superintendent	_____
Clerk	_____
Bricklayers	_____
Carpenters	_____
Cement Masons	_____
Electricians	_____
Iron Workers	_____
Laborers	_____
Operating Eng.	_____
Plumbers	_____
Pipe Fitters	_____
Sheet Metal	_____
Truck Drivers	_____
Total	_____

Equipment	Hrs.

Material Purchased

1 FEB. 20___   DAILY LOG   DAY _____

CONTRACTOR _____ JOB NAME _____ JOB NO._____

Work Performed Today _____

_____

_____

_____

_____

_____

_____

_____

_____

_____

_____

_____

_____

_____

Problems - Delays _____

_____

_____

_____

Sub-Contractor Progress _____

_____

_____

_____

Special Assignments _____

_____

_____

Extra Work	Authorized By	Approx. Price

Equipment Rented Today	Rented From	Rate

Supervisor's Signature _____

Weather_____

Temp. AM _____PM _____

Safety Meeting _____

Work Force	No.
Superintendent	_____
Clerk	_____
Bricklayers	_____
Carpenters	_____
Cement Masons	_____
Electricians	_____
Iron Workers	_____
Laborers	_____
Operating Eng.	_____
Plumbers	_____
Pipe Fitters	_____
Sheet Metal	_____
Truck Drivers	_____
Total	_____

Equipment	Hrs.

Material Purchased

DAY _____   DAILY LOG   20 ___ FEB. 2

CONTRACTOR _____ JOB NAME _____ JOB NO _____

Work Performed Today _____	Weather _____
	Temp. AM _____PM _____

| | Safety Meeting _____ |

Work Force	No.
Superintendent	_____
Clerk	_____
Bricklayers	_____
Carpenters	_____
Cement Masons	_____
Electricians	_____
Iron Workers	_____
Laborers	_____
Operating Eng.	_____
Plumbers	_____
Pipe Fitters	_____
Sheet Metal	_____
Truck Drivers	_____
Total	_____

Problems - Delays _____

Equipment	Hrs.

Sub-Contractor Progress _____

Special Assignments _____

Material Purchased

Extra Work	Authorized By	Approx. Price

Equipment Rented Today	Rented From	Rate

Supervisor's Signature _____

3 FEB. 20___   DAILY LOG   DAY _____

CONTRACTOR _____ JOB NAME _____ JOB NO. _____

Work Performed Today _____

_____

_____

_____

_____

_____

_____

_____

_____

_____

_____

_____

_____

_____

Problems - Delays _____

_____

_____

_____

_____

Sub-Contractor Progress _____

_____

_____

_____

Special Assignments _____

_____

_____

| Weather _____ |
| Temp. AM _____ PM _____ |
| Safety Meeting _____ |

Work Force	No.
Superintendent	_____
Clerk	_____
Bricklayers	_____
Carpenters	_____
Cement Masons	_____
Electricians	_____
Iron Workers	_____
Laborers	_____
Operating Eng.	_____
Plumbers	_____
Pipe Fitters	_____
Sheet Metal	_____
Truck Drivers	_____
Total	_____

Equipment	Hrs.

Material Purchased	

Extra Work	Authorized By	Approx. Price

Equipment Rented Today	Rented From	Rate

Supervisor's Signature _____

DAY _____ DAILY LOG 20___ FEB. 4

CONTRACTOR _____ JOB NAME _____ JOB NO _____

Work Performed Today _____

_____

_____

_____

_____

_____

_____

_____

_____

_____

_____

_____

_____

_____

_____

Problems - Delays _____

_____

_____

_____

_____

Sub-Contractor Progress _____

_____

_____

_____

Special Assignments _____

_____

_____

Weather	
Temp. AM _____ PM _____	
Safety Meeting _____	

Work Force	No.
Superintendent	_____
Clerk	_____
Bricklayers	_____
Carpenters	_____
Cement Masons	_____
Electricians	_____
Iron Workers	_____
Laborers	_____
Operating Eng.	_____
Plumbers	_____
Pipe Fitters	_____
Sheet Metal	_____
Truck Drivers	_____
Total	_____

Equipment	Hrs.

Material Purchased	

Extra Work	Authorized By	Approx. Price

Equipment Rented Today	Rented From	Rate

Supervisor's Signature _____

5 FEB. 20___   DAILY LOG   DAY _____

CONTRACTOR _____ JOB NAME _____ JOB NO._____

Work Performed Today _____

_____

_____

_____

_____

_____

_____

_____

_____

_____

_____

_____

_____

_____

_____

Problems - Delays _____

_____

_____

_____

Sub-Contractor Progress _____

_____

_____

_____

Special Assignments _____

_____

_____

_____

| Weather _____ |
| Temp. AM _____PM _____ |
| Safety Meeting _____ |

Work Force	No.
Superintendent	_____
Clerk	_____
Bricklayers	_____
Carpenters	_____
Cement Masons	_____
Electricians	_____
Iron Workers	_____
Laborers	_____
Operating Eng.	_____
Plumbers	_____
Pipe Fitters	_____
Sheet Metal	_____
Truck Drivers	_____
Total	_____

Equipment	Hrs.

Extra Work	Authorized By	Approx. Price

Equipment Rented Today	Rented From	Rate

Material Purchased

Supervisor's Signature _____

DAY _____   DAILY LOG   20___ FEB. 6

CONTRACTOR _____ JOB NAME _____ JOB NO _____

Work Performed Today _____

_____

_____

_____

_____

_____

_____

_____

_____

_____

_____

_____

_____

Problems - Delays _____

_____

_____

_____

Sub-Contractor Progress _____

_____

_____

_____

Special Assignments _____

_____

_____

Weather	
Temp. AM _____ PM _____	

Safety Meeting _____

Work Force	No.
Superintendent	_____
Clerk	_____
Bricklayers	_____
Carpenters	_____
Cement Masons	_____
Electricians	_____
Iron Workers	_____
Laborers	_____
Operating Eng.	_____
Plumbers	_____
Pipe Fitters	_____
Sheet Metal	_____
Truck Drivers	_____
Total	_____

Equipment	Hrs.

Extra Work	Authorized By	Approx. Price

Equipment Rented Today	Rented From	Rate

Material Purchased

Supervisor's Signature _____

7 FEB. 20___   DAILY LOG   DAY _____

CONTRACTOR _____ JOB NAME _____ JOB NO._____

Work Performed Today _____

_____

_____

_____

_____

_____

_____

_____

_____

_____

_____

_____

_____

Problems - Delays _____

_____

_____

_____

Sub-Contractor Progress _____

_____

_____

_____

Special Assignments _____

_____

_____

_____

Weather	_____
Temp. AM _____PM _____	

Safety Meeting _____

Work Force	No.
Superintendent	_____
Clerk	_____
Bricklayers	_____
Carpenters	_____
Cement Masons	_____
Electricians	_____
Iron Workers	_____
Laborers	_____
Operating Eng.	_____
Plumbers	_____
Pipe Fitters	_____
Sheet Metal	_____
Truck Drivers	_____
Total	_____

Equipment	Hrs.

Extra Work	Authorized By	Approx. Price

Equipment Rented Today	Rented From	Rate

Material Purchased

Supervisor's Signature _____

DAY _____   DAILY LOG   20___ FEB. 8

CONTRACTOR _____ JOB NAME _____ JOB NO _____

Work Performed Today _____	Weather _____
_____	Temp. AM _____PM _____
_____	Safety Meeting _____
_____	

Work Force	No.
Superintendent	_____
Clerk	_____
Bricklayers	_____
Carpenters	_____
Cement Masons	_____
Electricians	_____
Iron Workers	_____
Laborers	_____
Operating Eng.	_____
Plumbers	_____
Pipe Fitters	_____
Sheet Metal	_____
Truck Drivers	_____
Total	_____

Problems - Delays _____

Sub-Contractor Progress _____

Special Assignments _____

Equipment	Hrs.

Extra Work	Authorized By	Approx. Price

Equipment Rented Today	Rented From	Rate

Material Purchased

Supervisor's Signature _____

9 FEB. 20___   DAILY LOG   DAY _____

CONTRACTOR _____ JOB NAME _____ JOB NO._____

Work Performed Today _____	Weather _____
	Temp. AM _____ PM _____
	Safety Meeting _____
	Work Force **No.**
	Superintendent _____
	Clerk _____
	Bricklayers _____
	Carpenters _____
	Cement Masons _____
	Electricians _____
	Iron Workers _____
	Laborers _____
	Operating Eng. _____
	Plumbers _____
	Pipe Fitters _____
	Sheet Metal _____
	Truck Drivers _____
Problems - Delays _____	
	Total _____

Sub-Contractor Progress _____	Equipment	Hrs.

Special Assignments _____

Material Purchased

Extra Work	Authorized By	Approx. Price

Equipment Rented Today	Rented From	Rate

Supervisor's Signature _____

DAY _____   DAILY LOG   20___ FEB. 10

CONTRACTOR _____ JOB NAME _____ JOB NO _____

Work Performed Today _____

_____

_____

_____

_____

_____

_____

_____

_____

_____

_____

_____

_____

_____

Problems - Delays _____

_____

_____

_____

Sub-Contractor Progress _____

_____

_____

_____

Special Assignments _____

_____

_____

Weather	
Temp. AM _____ PM _____	
Safety Meeting _____	

Work Force	No.
Superintendent	_____
Clerk	_____
Bricklayers	_____
Carpenters	_____
Cement Masons	_____
Electricians	_____
Iron Workers	_____
Laborers	_____
Operating Eng.	_____
Plumbers	_____
Pipe Fitters	_____
Sheet Metal	_____
Truck Drivers	_____
Total	_____

Equipment	Hrs.

Extra Work	Authorized By	Approx. Price

Equipment Rented Today	Rented From	Rate

Material Purchased

Supervisor's Signature _____

11 FEB. 20___   DAILY LOG   DAY _____

CONTRACTOR _____ JOB NAME _____ JOB NO._____

Work Performed Today _____
_____
_____
_____
_____
_____
_____
_____
_____
_____
_____
_____
_____
_____

Problems - Delays _____
_____
_____
_____

Sub-Contractor Progress _____
_____
_____
_____

Special Assignments _____
_____
_____

Weather	_____
Temp. AM _____ PM	_____
Safety Meeting	_____

Work Force	No.
Superintendent	_____
Clerk	_____
Bricklayers	_____
Carpenters	_____
Cement Masons	_____
Electricians	_____
Iron Workers	_____
Laborers	_____
Operating Eng.	_____
Plumbers	_____
Pipe Fitters	_____
Sheet Metal	_____
Truck Drivers	_____
Total	_____

Equipment	Hrs.

Extra Work	Authorized By	Approx. Price

Equipment Rented Today	Rented From	Rate

Material Purchased

Supervisor's Signature _____

DAY _____   DAILY LOG   20___ FEB. 12

CONTRACTOR _____ JOB NAME _____ JOB NO _____

Work Performed Today _____	Weather _____
	Temp. AM _____ PM _____
	Safety Meeting _____

Work Force	No.
Superintendent	_____
Clerk	_____
Bricklayers	_____
Carpenters	_____
Cement Masons	_____
Electricians	_____
Iron Workers	_____
Laborers	_____
Operating Eng.	_____
Plumbers	_____
Pipe Fitters	_____
Sheet Metal	_____
Truck Drivers	_____
Total	_____

Problems - Delays _____

Equipment	Hrs.

Sub-Contractor Progress _____

Special Assignments _____

Extra Work	Authorized By	Approx. Price

Equipment Rented Today	Rented From	Rate

Material Purchased

Supervisor's Signature _____

13 FEB. 20___   DAILY LOG   DAY _____

CONTRACTOR _____ JOB NAME _____ JOB NO. _____

Work Performed Today _____

_____

_____

_____

_____

_____

_____

_____

_____

_____

_____

_____

_____

_____

_____

_____

Problems - Delays _____

_____

_____

_____

_____

Sub-Contractor Progress _____

_____

_____

_____

Special Assignments _____

_____

_____

_____

Weather	
Temp. AM _____ PM _____	
Safety Meeting _____	

Work Force	No.
Superintendent	_____
Clerk	_____
Bricklayers	_____
Carpenters	_____
Cement Masons	_____
Electricians	_____
Iron Workers	_____
Laborers	_____
Operating Eng.	_____
Plumbers	_____
Pipe Fitters	_____
Sheet Metal	_____
Truck Drivers	_____
Total	_____

Equipment	Hrs.

Extra Work	Authorized By	Approx. Price

Equipment Rented Today	Rented From	Rate

Material Purchased

Supervisor's Signature _____

DAY _____   DAILY LOG   20___ FEB. 14

CONTRACTOR _____ JOB NAME _____ JOB NO _____

| Work Performed Today _____ | Weather _____ |
| | Temp. AM _____ PM _____ |

| | Safety Meeting _____ |

Work Force	No.
Superintendent	_____
Clerk	_____
Bricklayers	_____
Carpenters	_____
Cement Masons	_____
Electricians	_____
Iron Workers	_____
Laborers	_____
Operating Eng.	_____
Plumbers	_____
Pipe Fitters	_____
Sheet Metal	_____
Truck Drivers	_____
Total	_____

Problems - Delays _____

Sub-Contractor Progress _____

Equipment	Hrs.

Special Assignments _____

Material Purchased	

Extra Work	Authorized By	Approx. Price

Equipment Rented Today	Rented From	Rate

Supervisor's Signature _____

15 FEB. 20___   DAILY LOG   DAY _____

CONTRACTOR _____ JOB NAME _____ JOB NO._____

Work Performed Today _____

_____

_____

_____

_____

_____

_____

_____

_____

_____

_____

_____

_____

_____

Problems - Delays _____

_____

_____

_____

Sub-Contractor Progress _____

_____

_____

_____

Special Assignments _____

_____

_____

_____

Weather _____

Temp. AM _____PM _____

Safety Meeting _____

Work Force	No.
Superintendent	_____
Clerk	_____
Bricklayers	_____
Carpenters	_____
Cement Masons	_____
Electricians	_____
Iron Workers	_____
Laborers	_____
Operating Eng.	_____
Plumbers	_____
Pipe Fitters	_____
Sheet Metal	_____
Truck Drivers	_____
Total	_____

Equipment	Hrs.

Extra Work	Authorized By	Approx. Price

Equipment Rented Today	Rented From	Rate

Material Purchased

Supervisor's Signature _____

DAY _____   DAILY LOG   20___ FEB. 16

CONTRACTOR _____ JOB NAME _____ JOB NO _____

Work Performed Today _____

_____

_____

_____

_____

_____

_____

_____

_____

_____

_____

_____

_____

_____

_____

Problems - Delays _____

_____

_____

_____

Sub-Contractor Progress _____

_____

_____

_____

Special Assignments _____

_____

_____

Weather	_____
Temp. AM _____ PM _____	
Safety Meeting _____	

Work Force	No.
Superintendent	_____
Clerk	_____
Bricklayers	_____
Carpenters	_____
Cement Masons	_____
Electricians	_____
Iron Workers	_____
Laborers	_____
Operating Eng.	_____
Plumbers	_____
Pipe Fitters	_____
Sheet Metal	_____
Truck Drivers	_____
Total	_____

Equipment	Hrs.

Extra Work	Authorized By	Approx. Price

Equipment Rented Today	Rented From	Rate

Material Purchased

Supervisor's Signature _____

17 FEB. 20___   DAILY LOG   DAY _____

CONTRACTOR _____ JOB NAME _____ JOB NO._____

Work Performed Today _____

_____

_____

_____

_____

_____

_____

_____

_____

_____

_____

_____

_____

_____

Problems - Delays _____

_____

_____

_____

Sub-Contractor Progress _____

_____

_____

_____

Special Assignments _____

_____

_____

Extra Work	Authorized By	Approx. Price

Equipment Rented Today	Rented From	Rate

Supervisor's Signature _____

Weather _____

Temp. AM _____PM _____

Safety Meeting _____

Work Force	No.
Superintendent	_____
Clerk	_____
Bricklayers	_____
Carpenters	_____
Cement Masons	_____
Electricians	_____
Iron Workers	_____
Laborers	_____
Operating Eng.	_____
Plumbers	_____
Pipe Fitters	_____
Sheet Metal	_____
Truck Drivers	_____
Total	_____

Equipment	Hrs.

Material Purchased

DAY _____   DAILY LOG   20___ FEB. 18

CONTRACTOR _____ JOB NAME _____ JOB NO _____

Work Performed Today _____

_____

_____

_____

_____

_____

_____

_____

_____

_____

_____

_____

_____

Problems - Delays _____

_____

_____

_____

Sub-Contractor Progress _____

_____

_____

Special Assignments _____

_____

_____

Weather		
Temp. AM _____ PM _____		
Safety Meeting _____		

Work Force	No.
Superintendent	_____
Clerk	_____
Bricklayers	_____
Carpenters	_____
Cement Masons	_____
Electricians	_____
Iron Workers	_____
Laborers	_____
Operating Eng.	_____
Plumbers	_____
Pipe Fitters	_____
Sheet Metal	_____
Truck Drivers	_____
Total	_____

Equipment	Hrs.

Extra Work	Authorized By	Approx. Price

Equipment Rented Today	Rented From	Rate

Material Purchased

Supervisor's Signature _____

19 FEB. 20___   DAILY LOG   DAY _____

CONTRACTOR _____ JOB NAME _____ JOB NO._____

Work Performed Today _____

_____

_____

_____

_____

_____

_____

_____

_____

_____

_____

_____

_____

_____

_____

Problems - Delays _____

_____

_____

_____

Sub-Contractor Progress _____

_____

_____

_____

Special Assignments _____

_____

_____

| Weather | _____ |
| Temp. AM _____ PM _____ |
| Safety Meeting _____ |

Work Force	No.
Superintendent	_____
Clerk	_____
Bricklayers	_____
Carpenters	_____
Cement Masons	_____
Electricians	_____
Iron Workers	_____
Laborers	_____
Operating Eng.	_____
Plumbers	_____
Pipe Fitters	_____
Sheet Metal	_____
Truck Drivers	_____
Total	_____

Equipment	Hrs.

Material Purchased

Extra Work	Authorized By	Approx. Price

Equipment Rented Today	Rented From	Rate

Supervisor's Signature _____

DAY _____   DAILY LOG   20___ FEB. 20

CONTRACTOR _____ JOB NAME _____ JOB NO _____

Work Performed Today _____

_____

_____

_____

_____

_____

_____

_____

_____

_____

_____

_____

_____

_____

_____

Problems - Delays _____

_____

_____

_____

Sub-Contractor Progress _____

_____

_____

_____

Special Assignments _____

_____

_____

Weather	_____
Temp. AM _____ PM _____	
Safety Meeting _____	

Work Force	No.
Superintendent	_____
Clerk	_____
Bricklayers	_____
Carpenters	_____
Cement Masons	_____
Electricians	_____
Iron Workers	_____
Laborers	_____
Operating Eng.	_____
Plumbers	_____
Pipe Fitters	_____
Sheet Metal	_____
Truck Drivers	_____
Total	_____

Equipment	Hrs.

Extra Work	Authorized By	Approx. Price

Equipment Rented Today	Rented From	Rate

Material Purchased

Supervisor's Signature _____

21 FEB. 20___   DAILY LOG   DAY _____

CONTRACTOR _____ JOB NAME _____ JOB NO. _____

Work Performed Today _____	Weather _____
	Temp. AM _____PM _____

Work Performed Today _____
_____
_____
_____
_____
_____
_____
_____
_____
_____
_____
_____
_____
_____
_____

Weather _____

Temp. AM _____PM _____

Safety Meeting _____

Work Force	No.
Superintendent	_____
Clerk	_____
Bricklayers	_____
Carpenters	_____
Cement Masons	_____
Electricians	_____
Iron Workers	_____
Laborers	_____
Operating Eng.	_____
Plumbers	_____
Pipe Fitters	_____
Sheet Metal	_____
Truck Drivers	_____
Total	_____

Problems - Delays _____
_____
_____
_____

Sub-Contractor Progress _____
_____
_____
_____

Equipment	Hrs.

Special Assignments _____
_____
_____

Extra Work	Authorized By	Approx. Price

Equipment Rented Today	Rented From	Rate

Material Purchased

Supervisor's Signature _____

DAY _____   DAILY LOG   20___ FEB. 22

CONTRACTOR _____ JOB NAME _____ JOB NO _____

Work Performed Today _____

_____

_____

_____

_____

_____

_____

_____

_____

_____

_____

_____

_____

_____

Problems - Delays _____

_____

_____

_____

Sub-Contractor Progress _____

_____

_____

_____

Special Assignments _____

_____

_____

Extra Work	Authorized By	Approx. Price

Equipment Rented Today	Rented From	Rate

Supervisor's Signature _____

Weather _____

Temp. AM _____ PM _____

Safety Meeting _____

Work Force	No.
Superintendent	_____
Clerk	_____
Bricklayers	_____
Carpenters	_____
Cement Masons	_____
Electricians	_____
Iron Workers	_____
Laborers	_____
Operating Eng.	_____
Plumbers	_____
Pipe Fitters	_____
Sheet Metal	_____
Truck Drivers	_____
Total	_____

Equipment	Hrs.

Material Purchased

23 FEB. 20___   DAILY LOG   DAY _____

CONTRACTOR _____ JOB NAME _____ JOB NO._____

Work Performed Today _____	Weather _____
_____	Temp. AM _____PM _____
_____	Safety Meeting _____

Work Force	No.
Superintendent	_____
Clerk	_____
Bricklayers	_____
Carpenters	_____
Cement Masons	_____
Electricians	_____
Iron Workers	_____
Laborers	_____
Operating Eng.	_____
Plumbers	_____
Pipe Fitters	_____
Sheet Metal	_____
Truck Drivers	_____
Total	_____

Problems - Delays _____

Equipment	Hrs.

Sub-Contractor Progress _____

Special Assignments _____

Material Purchased

Extra Work	Authorized By	Approx. Price

Equipment Rented Today	Rented From	Rate

Supervisor's Signature _____

DAY _____   DAILY LOG   20___ FEB. 24

CONTRACTOR _____ JOB NAME _____ JOB NO _____

Work Performed Today _____

_____

_____

_____

_____

_____

_____

_____

_____

_____

_____

_____

_____

_____

Problems - Delays _____

_____

_____

_____

Sub-Contractor Progress _____

_____

_____

_____

Special Assignments _____

_____

_____

_____

Weather _____

Temp. AM _____ PM _____

Safety Meeting _____

Work Force	No.
Superintendent	_____
Clerk	_____
Bricklayers	_____
Carpenters	_____
Cement Masons	_____
Electricians	_____
Iron Workers	_____
Laborers	_____
Operating Eng.	_____
Plumbers	_____
Pipe Fitters	_____
Sheet Metal	_____
Truck Drivers	_____
Total	_____

Equipment	Hrs.

Extra Work	Authorized By	Approx. Price

Equipment Rented Today	Rented From	Rate

Material Purchased

Supervisor's Signature _____

25 FEB. 20___   DAILY LOG   DAY _____

CONTRACTOR _____ JOB NAME _____ JOB NO._____

Work Performed Today _____

_____

_____

_____

_____

_____

_____

_____

_____

_____

_____

_____

_____

Problems - Delays _____

_____

_____

_____

Sub-Contractor Progress _____

_____

_____

_____

Special Assignments _____

_____

_____

Extra Work	Authorized By	Approx. Price

Equipment Rented Today	Rented From	Rate

Supervisor's Signature _____

Weather _____

Temp. AM _____PM _____

Safety Meeting _____

Work Force	No.
Superintendent	
Clerk	
Bricklayers	
Carpenters	
Cement Masons	
Electricians	
Iron Workers	
Laborers	
Operating Eng.	
Plumbers	
Pipe Fitters	
Sheet Metal	
Truck Drivers	
Total	

Equipment	Hrs.

Material Purchased

DAY _____   DAILY LOG   20___ FEB. 26

CONTRACTOR _____ JOB NAME _____ JOB NO _____

Work Performed Today _____

_____

_____

_____

_____

_____

_____

_____

_____

_____

_____

_____

_____

_____

Problems - Delays _____

_____

_____

_____

Sub-Contractor Progress _____

_____

_____

Special Assignments _____

_____

_____

Weather	
Temp. AM _____ PM _____	
Safety Meeting _____	

Work Force	No.
Superintendent	_____
Clerk	_____
Bricklayers	_____
Carpenters	_____
Cement Masons	_____
Electricians	_____
Iron Workers	_____
Laborers	_____
Operating Eng.	_____
Plumbers	_____
Pipe Fitters	_____
Sheet Metal	_____
Truck Drivers	_____
Total	_____

Equipment	Hrs.

Extra Work	Authorized By	Approx. Price

Equipment Rented Today	Rented From	Rate

Material Purchased

Supervisor's Signature _____

27 FEB. 20___   DAILY LOG   DAY _____

CONTRACTOR _____ JOB NAME _____ JOB NO._____

Work Performed Today _____

_____

_____

_____

_____

_____

_____

_____

_____

_____

_____

_____

_____

Problems - Delays _____

_____

_____

_____

Sub-Contractor Progress _____

_____

_____

Special Assignments _____

_____

_____

Extra Work	Authorized By	Approx. Price

Equipment Rented Today	Rented From	Rate

Supervisor's Signature _____

Weather_____

Temp. AM _____PM _____

Safety Meeting _____

Work Force	No.
Superintendent	_____
Clerk	_____
Bricklayers	_____
Carpenters	_____
Cement Masons	_____
Electricians	_____
Iron Workers	_____
Laborers	_____
Operating Eng.	_____
Plumbers	_____
Pipe Fitters	_____
Sheet Metal	_____
Truck Drivers	_____
Total	_____

Equipment	Hrs.

Material Purchased	

DAY _____   DAILY LOG   20 ___ FEB. 28

CONTRACTOR _____ JOB NAME _____ JOB NO _____

Work Performed Today _____	Weather _____
_____	Temp. AM _____ PM _____
_____	
_____	Safety Meeting _____

	Work Force	**No.**
	Superintendent	_____
	Clerk	_____
	Bricklayers	_____
	Carpenters	_____
	Cement Masons	_____
	Electricians	_____
	Iron Workers	_____
	Laborers	_____
	Operating Eng.	_____
	Plumbers	_____
	Pipe Fitters	_____
	Sheet Metal	
	Truck Drivers	

Problems - Delays _____
_____
_____
_____

| **Total** | _____ |

Sub-Contractor Progress _____
_____
_____
_____

Equipment	Hrs.

Special Assignments _____
_____
_____

Extra Work	Authorized By	Approx. Price

Equipment Rented Today	Rented From	Rate

Material Purchased

Supervisor's Signature _____

29 FEB. 20___   DAILY LOG   DAY _____

CONTRACTOR _____ JOB NAME _____ JOB NO. _____

Work Performed Today _____

_____

_____

_____

_____

_____

_____

_____

_____

_____

_____

_____

_____

_____

Problems - Delays _____

_____

_____

_____

Sub-Contractor Progress _____

_____

_____

_____

Special Assignments _____

_____

_____

| Weather _____ |
| Temp. AM _____PM _____ |
| Safety Meeting _____ |

Work Force	No.
Superintendent	_____
Clerk	_____
Bricklayers	_____
Carpenters	_____
Cement Masons	_____
Electricians	_____
Iron Workers	_____
Laborers	_____
Operating Eng.	_____
Plumbers	_____
Pipe Fitters	_____
Sheet Metal	_____
Truck Drivers	_____
Total	_____

Equipment	Hrs.

Material Purchased	

Extra Work	Authorized By	Approx. Price

Equipment Rented Today	Rented From	Rate

Supervisor's Signature _____

DAY _____   DAILY LOG   20___ MAR. 1

CONTRACTOR _____ JOB NAME _____ JOB NO _____

Work Performed Today _____

_____

_____

_____

_____

_____

_____

_____

_____

_____

_____

_____

_____

_____

_____

Problems - Delays _____

_____

_____

_____

Sub-Contractor Progress _____

_____

_____

_____

Special Assignments _____

_____

_____

_____

Extra Work	Authorized By	Approx. Price

Equipment Rented Today	Rented From	Rate

Supervisor's Signature _____

Weather _____

Temp. AM _____ PM _____

Safety Meeting _____

Work Force	No.
Superintendent	_____
Clerk	_____
Bricklayers	_____
Carpenters	_____
Cement Masons	_____
Electricians	_____
Iron Workers	_____
Laborers	_____
Operating Eng.	_____
Plumbers	_____
Pipe Fitters	_____
Sheet Metal	_____
Truck Drivers	_____
Total	_____

Equipment	Hrs.

Material Purchased

2 MAR. 20___   DAILY LOG   DAY _____

CONTRACTOR _____ JOB NAME _____ JOB NO._____

Work Performed Today _____	Weather _____

Work Performed Today _____

Weather _____

Temp. AM _____PM _____

Safety Meeting _____

Work Force	No.
Superintendent	_____
Clerk	_____
Bricklayers	_____
Carpenters	_____
Cement Masons	_____
Electricians	_____
Iron Workers	_____
Laborers	_____
Operating Eng.	_____
Plumbers	_____
Pipe Fitters	_____
Sheet Metal	_____
Truck Drivers	_____
Total	_____

Problems - Delays _____

Equipment	Hrs.

Sub-Contractor Progress _____

Special Assignments _____

Extra Work	Authorized By	Approx. Price

Equipment Rented Today	Rented From	Rate

Material Purchased

Supervisor's Signature _____

DAY _____   DAILY LOG   20___ MAR. 3

CONTRACTOR _____ JOB NAME _____ JOB NO _____

Work Performed Today _____	Weather _____
_____	Temp. AM _____PM _____
_____	
_____	Safety Meeting _____

Work Force	No.
Superintendent	_____
Clerk	_____
Bricklayers	_____
Carpenters	_____
Cement Masons	_____
Electricians	_____
Iron Workers	_____
Laborers	_____
Operating Eng.	_____
Plumbers	_____
Pipe Fitters	_____
Sheet Metal	_____
Truck Drivers	_____
Total	_____

Problems - Delays _____

Sub-Contractor Progress _____

Equipment	Hrs.

Special Assignments _____

Extra Work	Authorized By	Approx. Price

Equipment Rented Today	Rented From	Rate

Material Purchased

Supervisor's Signature _____

4 MAR. 20___   DAILY LOG   DAY _____

CONTRACTOR _____ JOB NAME _____ JOB NO. _____

Work Performed Today _____	Weather _____
	Temp. AM _____ PM _____
	Safety Meeting _____

Work Force	No.
Superintendent	_____
Clerk	_____
Bricklayers	_____
Carpenters	_____
Cement Masons	_____
Electricians	_____
Iron Workers	_____
Laborers	_____
Operating Eng.	_____
Plumbers	_____
Pipe Fitters	_____
Sheet Metal	_____
Truck Drivers	_____
Total	_____

Problems - Delays _____

Sub-Contractor Progress _____

Special Assignments _____

Equipment	Hrs.

Extra Work	Authorized By	Approx. Price

Equipment Rented Today	Rented From	Rate

Material Purchased

Supervisor's Signature _____

DAY _____   DAILY LOG   20___ MAR. 5

CONTRACTOR _____ JOB NAME _____ JOB NO _____

Work Performed Today _____

_____

_____

_____

_____

_____

_____

_____

_____

_____

_____

_____

_____

_____

Problems - Delays _____

_____

_____

_____

Sub-Contractor Progress _____

_____

_____

_____

Special Assignments _____

_____

_____

| Weather _____ |
| Temp. AM _____PM ____ |
| Safety Meeting _____ |

Work Force	No.
Superintendent	_____
Clerk	_____
Bricklayers	_____
Carpenters	_____
Cement Masons	_____
Electricians	_____
Iron Workers	_____
Laborers	_____
Operating Eng.	_____
Plumbers	_____
Pipe Fitters	_____
Sheet Metal	_____
Truck Drivers	_____
Total	_____

Equipment	Hrs.

Material Purchased

Extra Work	Authorized By	Approx. Price

Equipment Rented Today	Rented From	Rate

Supervisor's Signature _____

6 MAR. 20___   DAILY LOG   DAY _____

CONTRACTOR _____ JOB NAME _____ JOB NO. _____

Work Performed Today _____

_____

_____

_____

_____

_____

_____

_____

_____

_____

_____

_____

_____

_____

Problems - Delays _____

_____

_____

_____

Sub-Contractor Progress _____

_____

_____

_____

Special Assignments _____

_____

_____

Weather	_____
Temp. AM _____	PM _____
Safety Meeting _____	

Work Force	No.
Superintendent	_____
Clerk	_____
Bricklayers	_____
Carpenters	_____
Cement Masons	_____
Electricians	_____
Iron Workers	_____
Laborers	_____
Operating Eng.	_____
Plumbers	_____
Pipe Fitters	_____
Sheet Metal	_____
Truck Drivers	_____
Total	_____

Equipment	Hrs.

Extra Work	Authorized By	Approx. Price

Equipment Rented Today	Rented From	Rate

Material Purchased

Supervisor's Signature _____

DAY _____   DAILY LOG   20___ MAR. 7

CONTRACTOR _____ JOB NAME _____ JOB NO _____

Work Performed Today _____		Weather_____
_____		Temp. AM _____PM _____
_____		Safety Meeting _____
_____		

Work Force	No.
Superintendent	_____
Clerk	_____
Bricklayers	_____
Carpenters	_____
Cement Masons	_____
Electricians	_____
Iron Workers	_____
Laborers	_____
Operating Eng.	_____
Plumbers	_____
Pipe Fitters	_____
Sheet Metal	_____
Truck Drivers	_____
Total	_____

Problems - Delays _____

Equipment	Hrs.

Sub-Contractor Progress _____

Special Assignments _____

Extra Work	Authorized By	Approx. Price

Material Purchased	

Equipment Rented Today	Rented From	Rate

Supervisor's Signature _____

8 MAR. 20___   DAILY LOG   DAY _____

CONTRACTOR _____ JOB NAME _____ JOB NO._____

Work Performed Today _____

_____

_____

_____

_____

_____

_____

_____

_____

_____

_____

_____

_____

_____

_____

Problems - Delays _____

_____

_____

_____

Sub-Contractor Progress _____

_____

_____

_____

Special Assignments _____

_____

_____

Weather	_____
Temp. AM _____ PM _____	
Safety Meeting _____	

Work Force	No.
Superintendent	_____
Clerk	_____
Bricklayers	_____
Carpenters	_____
Cement Masons	_____
Electricians	_____
Iron Workers	_____
Laborers	_____
Operating Eng.	_____
Plumbers	_____
Pipe Fitters	_____
Sheet Metal	_____
Truck Drivers	_____
Total	_____

Equipment	Hrs.

Extra Work	Authorized By	Approx. Price

Equipment Rented Today	Rented From	Rate

Material Purchased

Supervisor's Signature _____

DAY _____   DAILY LOG   20___ MAR. 9

CONTRACTOR _____ JOB NAME _____ JOB NO _____

Work Performed Today _____

_____

_____

_____

_____

_____

_____

_____

_____

_____

_____

_____

_____

_____

_____

Problems - Delays _____

_____

_____

_____

Sub-Contractor Progress _____

_____

_____

_____

Special Assignments _____

_____

_____

Weather	
Temp. AM _____ PM _____	
Safety Meeting _____	

Work Force	No.
Superintendent	_____
Clerk	_____
Bricklayers	_____
Carpenters	_____
Cement Masons	_____
Electricians	_____
Iron Workers	_____
Laborers	_____
Operating Eng.	_____
Plumbers	_____
Pipe Fitters	_____
Sheet Metal	_____
Truck Drivers	_____
Total	_____

Equipment	Hrs.

Extra Work	Authorized By	Approx. Price

Equipment Rented Today	Rented From	Rate

Material Purchased

Supervisor's Signature _____

10 MAR. 20____   DAILY LOG   DAY _____

CONTRACTOR _____ JOB NAME _____ JOB NO._____

| Work Performed Today _____ | Weather_____ |

Temp. AM _____PM _____

Safety Meeting _____

Work Force	**No.**
Superintendent	_____
Clerk	_____
Bricklayers	_____
Carpenters	_____
Cement Masons	_____
Electricians	_____
Iron Workers	_____
Laborers	_____
Operating Eng.	_____
Plumbers	_____
Pipe Fitters	_____
Sheet Metal	_____
Truck Drivers	_____
Total	_____

Problems - Delays _____

Sub-Contractor Progress _____

Equipment	Hrs.

Special Assignments _____

Extra Work	Authorized By	Approx. Price

Equipment Rented Today	Rented From	Rate

Material Purchased

Supervisor's Signature _____

DAY _____   DAILY LOG   20___ MAR. 11

CONTRACTOR _____ JOB NAME _____ JOB NO _____

Work Performed Today _____

_____

_____

_____

_____

_____

_____

_____

_____

_____

_____

_____

_____

_____

_____

_____

Problems - Delays _____

_____

_____

_____

Sub-Contractor Progress _____

_____

_____

_____

Special Assignments _____

_____

_____

Extra Work	Authorized By	Approx. Price

Equipment Rented Today	Rented From	Rate

Supervisor's Signature _____

Weather _____

Temp. AM _____ PM _____

Safety Meeting _____

Work Force	No.
Superintendent	
Clerk	
Bricklayers	
Carpenters	
Cement Masons	
Electricians	
Iron Workers	
Laborers	
Operating Eng.	
Plumbers	
Pipe Fitters	
Sheet Metal	
Truck Drivers	
Total	

Equipment	Hrs.

Material Purchased

12 MAR. 20___   DAILY LOG   DAY _____

CONTRACTOR _____ JOB NAME _____ JOB NO._____

Work Performed Today _____

_____

_____

_____

_____

_____

_____

_____

_____

_____

_____

_____

_____

_____

Problems - Delays _____

_____

_____

_____

Sub-Contractor Progress _____

_____

_____

_____

Special Assignments _____

_____

_____

Extra Work	Authorized By	Approx. Price

Equipment Rented Today	Rented From	Rate

Supervisor's Signature _____

Weather _____

Temp. AM _____PM _____

Safety Meeting _____

Work Force	No.
Superintendent	
Clerk	
Bricklayers	
Carpenters	
Cement Masons	
Electricians	
Iron Workers	
Laborers	
Operating Eng.	
Plumbers	
Pipe Fitters	
Sheet Metal	
Truck Drivers	
Total	

Equipment	Hrs.

Material Purchased

DAY _____ DAILY LOG 20___ MAR. 13

CONTRACTOR _____ JOB NAME _____ JOB NO _____

Work Performed Today _____

_____

_____

_____

_____

_____

_____

_____

_____

_____

_____

_____

_____

Problems - Delays _____

_____

_____

_____

Sub-Contractor Progress _____

_____

_____

_____

Special Assignments _____

_____

_____

Weather	
Temp. AM _____ PM _____	
Safety Meeting _____	

Work Force	No.
Superintendent	_____
Clerk	_____
Bricklayers	_____
Carpenters	_____
Cement Masons	_____
Electricians	_____
Iron Workers	_____
Laborers	_____
Operating Eng.	_____
Plumbers	_____
Pipe Fitters	_____
Sheet Metal	_____
Truck Drivers	_____
Total	_____

Equipment	Hrs.

Extra Work	Authorized By	Approx. Price

Equipment Rented Today	Rented From	Rate

Material Purchased

Supervisor's Signature _____

14 MAR. 20___   DAILY LOG   DAY _____

CONTRACTOR _____ JOB NAME _____ JOB NO._____

Work Performed Today _____

_____

_____

_____

_____

_____

_____

_____

_____

_____

_____

_____

_____

_____

_____

Problems - Delays _____

_____

_____

_____

Sub-Contractor Progress _____

_____

_____

_____

Special Assignments _____

_____

_____

Weather	
Temp. AM _____ PM _____	
Safety Meeting _____	

Work Force	No.
Superintendent	_____
Clerk	_____
Bricklayers	_____
Carpenters	_____
Cement Masons	_____
Electricians	_____
Iron Workers	_____
Laborers	_____
Operating Eng.	_____
Plumbers	_____
Pipe Fitters	_____
Sheet Metal	_____
Truck Drivers	_____
Total	_____

Equipment	Hrs.

Material Purchased

Extra Work	Authorized By	Approx. Price

Equipment Rented Today	Rented From	Rate

Supervisor's Signature _____

DAY _____   DAILY LOG   20___ MAR. 15

CONTRACTOR _____ JOB NAME _____ JOB NO _____

Work Performed Today _____

_____

_____

_____

_____

_____

_____

_____

_____

_____

_____

_____

_____

_____

Problems - Delays _____

_____

_____

_____

Sub-Contractor Progress _____

_____

_____

_____

Special Assignments _____

_____

_____

Weather	
Temp. AM _____ PM _____	
Safety Meeting _____	

Work Force	No.
Superintendent	_____
Clerk	_____
Bricklayers	_____
Carpenters	_____
Cement Masons	_____
Electricians	_____
Iron Workers	_____
Laborers	_____
Operating Eng.	_____
Plumbers	_____
Pipe Fitters	_____
Sheet Metal	_____
Truck Drivers	_____
Total	_____

Equipment	Hrs.

Extra Work	Authorized By	Approx. Price

Equipment Rented Today	Rented From	Rate

Material Purchased

Supervisor's Signature _____

16 MAR. 20___   DAILY LOG   DAY _____

CONTRACTOR _____ JOB NAME _____ JOB NO._____

Work Performed Today _____

_____

_____

_____

_____

_____

_____

_____

_____

_____

_____

_____

_____

Problems - Delays _____

_____

_____

_____

Sub-Contractor Progress _____

_____

_____

_____

Special Assignments _____

_____

_____

Extra Work	Authorized By	Approx. Price

Equipment Rented Today	Rented From	Rate

Supervisor's Signature _____

Weather _____

Temp. AM _____PM _____

Safety Meeting _____

Work Force	No.
Superintendent	
Clerk	
Bricklayers	
Carpenters	
Cement Masons	
Electricians	
Iron Workers	
Laborers	
Operating Eng.	
Plumbers	
Pipe Fitters	
Sheet Metal	
Truck Drivers	
Total	

Equipment	Hrs.

Material Purchased

DAY _____   DAILY LOG   20___ MAR. 17

CONTRACTOR _____ JOB NAME _____ JOB NO _____

Work Performed Today _____

_____

_____

_____

_____

_____

_____

_____

_____

_____

_____

_____

_____

_____

Problems - Delays _____

_____

_____

_____

Sub-Contractor Progress _____

_____

_____

_____

Special Assignments _____

_____

_____

Extra Work	Authorized By	Approx. Price

Equipment Rented Today	Rented From	Rate

Supervisor's Signature _____

Weather _____

Temp. AM _____PM _____

Safety Meeting _____

Work Force	No.
Superintendent	_____
Clerk	_____
Bricklayers	_____
Carpenters	_____
Cement Masons	_____
Electricians	_____
Iron Workers	_____
Laborers	_____
Operating Eng.	_____
Plumbers	_____
Pipe Fitters	_____
Sheet Metal	_____
Truck Drivers	_____
Total	_____

Equipment	Hrs.

Material Purchased

18 MAR. 20___   DAILY LOG   DAY _____

CONTRACTOR _____ JOB NAME _____ JOB NO._____

Work Performed Today _____

_____

_____

_____

_____

_____

_____

_____

_____

_____

_____

_____

_____

_____

Problems - Delays _____

_____

_____

_____

Sub-Contractor Progress _____

_____

_____

_____

Special Assignments _____

_____

_____

Extra Work	Authorized By	Approx. Price

Equipment Rented Today	Rented From	Rate

Supervisor's Signature _____

Weather_____

Temp. AM _____PM _____

Safety Meeting _____

Work Force	No.
Superintendent	
Clerk	
Bricklayers	
Carpenters	
Cement Masons	
Electricians	
Iron Workers	
Laborers	
Operating Eng.	
Plumbers	
Pipe Fitters	
Sheet Metal	
Truck Drivers	
Total	

Equipment	Hrs.

Material Purchased

DAY _____   DAILY LOG   20___ MAR. 19

CONTRACTOR _____ JOB NAME _____ JOB NO _____

Work Performed Today _____	Weather _____
_____	Temp. AM _____PM _____
_____	Safety Meeting _____

Work Force	No.
Superintendent	_____
Clerk	_____
Bricklayers	_____
Carpenters	_____
Cement Masons	_____
Electricians	_____
Iron Workers	_____
Laborers	_____
Operating Eng.	_____
Plumbers	_____
Pipe Fitters	_____
Sheet Metal	_____
Truck Drivers	_____
Total	_____

Problems - Delays _____

Equipment	Hrs.

Sub-Contractor Progress _____

Special Assignments _____

Extra Work	Authorized By	Approx. Price

Material Purchased

Equipment Rented Today	Rented From	Rate

Supervisor's Signature _____

20 MAR. 20___   DAILY LOG   DAY _____

CONTRACTOR _____ JOB NAME _____ JOB NO._____

Work Performed Today _____

_____

_____

_____

_____

_____

_____

_____

_____

_____

_____

_____

_____

_____

Problems - Delays _____

_____

_____

_____

Sub-Contractor Progress _____

_____

_____

_____

Special Assignments _____

_____

_____

Weather		
Temp. AM _____ PM _____		
Safety Meeting _____		

Work Force	No.
Superintendent	_____
Clerk	_____
Bricklayers	_____
Carpenters	_____
Cement Masons	_____
Electricians	_____
Iron Workers	_____
Laborers	_____
Operating Eng.	_____
Plumbers	_____
Pipe Fitters	_____
Sheet Metal	_____
Truck Drivers	_____
Total	_____

Equipment	Hrs.

Extra Work	Authorized By	Approx. Price

Equipment Rented Today	Rented From	Rate

Material Purchased

Supervisor's Signature _____

DAY _____   DAILY LOG   20____ MAR. 21

CONTRACTOR _____ JOB NAME _____ JOB NO _____

Work Performed Today _____	Weather _____
	Temp. AM _____ PM _____
_____	
_____	Safety Meeting _____
_____	

Work Force	No.
Superintendent	_____
Clerk	_____
Bricklayers	_____
Carpenters	_____
Cement Masons	_____
Electricians	_____
Iron Workers	_____
Laborers	_____
Operating Eng.	_____
Plumbers	_____
Pipe Fitters	_____
Sheet Metal	_____
Truck Drivers	_____
Total	_____

Problems - Delays _____

Sub-Contractor Progress _____

Equipment	Hrs.

Special Assignments _____

Extra Work	Authorized By	Approx. Price

Equipment Rented Today	Rented From	Rate

Material Purchased

Supervisor's Signature _____

22 MAR. 20___   DAILY LOG   DAY _____

CONTRACTOR _____ JOB NAME _____ JOB NO._____

Work Performed Today _____

_____

_____

_____

_____

_____

_____

_____

_____

_____

_____

_____

_____

_____

Problems - Delays _____

_____

_____

_____

Sub-Contractor Progress _____

_____

_____

_____

Special Assignments _____

_____

_____

Weather	_____
Temp. AM _____PM _____	
Safety Meeting _____	

Work Force	No.
Superintendent	_____
Clerk	_____
Bricklayers	_____
Carpenters	_____
Cement Masons	_____
Electricians	_____
Iron Workers	_____
Laborers	_____
Operating Eng.	_____
Plumbers	_____
Pipe Fitters	_____
Sheet Metal	_____
Truck Drivers	_____
Total	_____

Equipment	Hrs.

Material Purchased

Extra Work	Authorized By	Approx. Price

Equipment Rented Today	Rented From	Rate

Supervisor's Signature _____

DAY _____   DAILY LOG   20___ MAR. 23

CONTRACTOR _____ JOB NAME _____ JOB NO _____

Work Performed Today _____

_____

_____

_____

_____

_____

_____

_____

_____

_____

_____

_____

_____

_____

Problems - Delays _____

_____

_____

_____

Sub-Contractor Progress _____

_____

_____

_____

Special Assignments _____

_____

_____

Extra Work	Authorized By	Approx. Price

Equipment Rented Today	Rented From	Rate

Supervisor's Signature _____

Weather _____

Temp. AM _____PM _____

Safety Meeting _____

Work Force	No.
Superintendent	_____
Clerk	_____
Bricklayers	_____
Carpenters	_____
Cement Masons	_____
Electricians	_____
Iron Workers	_____
Laborers	_____
Operating Eng.	_____
Plumbers	_____
Pipe Fitters	_____
Sheet Metal	_____
Truck Drivers	_____
Total	_____

Equipment	Hrs.

Material Purchased

24 MAR. 20___   DAILY LOG   DAY _____

CONTRACTOR _____ JOB NAME _____ JOB NO._____

Work Performed Today _____

_____

_____

_____

_____

_____

_____

_____

_____

_____

_____

_____

_____

_____

Problems - Delays _____

_____

_____

_____

Sub-Contractor Progress _____

_____

_____

_____

Special Assignments _____

_____

_____

Weather	_____
Temp. AM _____ PM _____	
Safety Meeting _____	

Work Force	No.
Superintendent	_____
Clerk	_____
Bricklayers	_____
Carpenters	_____
Cement Masons	_____
Electricians	_____
Iron Workers	_____
Laborers	_____
Operating Eng.	_____
Plumbers	_____
Pipe Fitters	_____
Sheet Metal	_____
Truck Drivers	_____
Total	_____

Equipment	Hrs.

Extra Work	Authorized By	Approx. Price

Equipment Rented Today	Rented From	Rate

Material Purchased

Supervisor's Signature _____

DAY _____   DAILY LOG   20___ MAR. 25

CONTRACTOR _____ JOB NAME _____ JOB NO _____

Work Performed Today _____

_____

_____

_____

_____

_____

_____

_____

_____

_____

_____

_____

Problems - Delays _____

_____

_____

_____

Sub-Contractor Progress _____

_____

_____

Special Assignments _____

_____

_____

Extra Work	Authorized By	Approx. Price

Equipment Rented Today	Rented From	Rate

Supervisor's Signature _____

Weather _____

Temp. AM _____ PM _____

Safety Meeting _____

Work Force	No.
Superintendent	_____
Clerk	_____
Bricklayers	_____
Carpenters	_____
Cement Masons	_____
Electricians	_____
Iron Workers	_____
Laborers	_____
Operating Eng.	_____
Plumbers	_____
Pipe Fitters	_____
Sheet Metal	_____
Truck Drivers	_____
Total	_____

Equipment	Hrs.

Material Purchased

26 MAR. 20___   DAILY LOG   DAY _____

CONTRACTOR _____ JOB NAME _____ JOB NO._____

Work Performed Today _____

_____

_____

_____

_____

_____

_____

_____

_____

_____

_____

_____

_____

_____

Problems - Delays _____

_____

_____

_____

Sub-Contractor Progress _____

_____

_____

_____

Special Assignments _____

_____

_____

| Weather _____ |
| Temp. AM _____ PM _____ |
| Safety Meeting _____ |

Work Force	No.
Superintendent	_____
Clerk	_____
Bricklayers	_____
Carpenters	_____
Cement Masons	_____
Electricians	_____
Iron Workers	_____
Laborers	_____
Operating Eng.	_____
Plumbers	_____
Pipe Fitters	_____
Sheet Metal	_____
Truck Drivers	_____
Total	_____

Equipment	Hrs.

Material Purchased

Extra Work	Authorized By	Approx. Price

Equipment Rented Today	Rented From	Rate

Supervisor's Signature _____

DAY _____   DAILY LOG   20___ MAR. 27

CONTRACTOR _____ JOB NAME _____ JOB NO _____

Work Performed Today _____

_____

_____

_____

_____

_____

_____

_____

_____

_____

_____

_____

Problems - Delays _____

_____

_____

_____

Sub-Contractor Progress _____

_____

_____

_____

Special Assignments _____

_____

_____

| Weather | _____ |
| Temp. AM _____ PM _____ |
| Safety Meeting _____ |

Work Force	No.
Superintendent	_____
Clerk	_____
Bricklayers	_____
Carpenters	_____
Cement Masons	_____
Electricians	_____
Iron Workers	_____
Laborers	_____
Operating Eng.	_____
Plumbers	_____
Pipe Fitters	_____
Sheet Metal	_____
Truck Drivers	_____
Total	_____

Equipment	Hrs.

Extra Work	Authorized By	Approx. Price

Equipment Rented Today	Rented From	Rate

Material Purchased

Supervisor's Signature _____

28 MAR. 20____   DAILY LOG   DAY _____

CONTRACTOR _____ JOB NAME _____ JOB NO. _____

Work Performed Today _____	Weather _____
_____	Temp. AM _____ PM _____
_____	Safety Meeting _____
_____	**Work Force** No.
_____	Superintendent _____
_____	Clerk _____
_____	Bricklayers _____
_____	Carpenters _____
_____	Cement Masons _____
_____	Electricians _____
_____	Iron Workers _____
_____	Laborers _____
_____	Operating Eng. _____
_____	Plumbers _____
_____	Pipe Fitters _____
_____	Sheet Metal _____
_____	Truck Drivers _____
Problems - Delays _____	
_____	
_____	
_____	**Total** _____
Sub-Contractor Progress _____	Equipment Hrs.
_____	
_____	
_____	
Special Assignments _____	
_____	
_____	

Extra Work	Authorized By	Approx. Price	Material Purchased
Equipment Rented Today	Rented From	Rate	

Supervisor's Signature _____

DAY _____   DAILY LOG   20___ MAR. 29

CONTRACTOR _____ JOB NAME _____ JOB NO _____

Work Performed Today _____

_____

_____

_____

_____

_____

_____

_____

_____

_____

_____

_____

_____

Problems - Delays _____

_____

_____

_____

Sub-Contractor Progress _____

_____

_____

Special Assignments _____

_____

_____

Weather		
Temp. AM _____ PM _____		
Safety Meeting _____		

Work Force	No.
Superintendent	_____
Clerk	_____
Bricklayers	_____
Carpenters	_____
Cement Masons	_____
Electricians	_____
Iron Workers	_____
Laborers	_____
Operating Eng.	_____
Plumbers	_____
Pipe Fitters	_____
Sheet Metal	_____
Truck Drivers	_____
Total	_____

Equipment	Hrs.

Extra Work	Authorized By	Approx. Price

Equipment Rented Today	Rented From	Rate

Material Purchased

Supervisor's Signature _____

30 MAR. 20___   DAILY LOG   DAY _____

CONTRACTOR _____ JOB NAME _____ JOB NO._____

Work Performed Today _____

_____

_____

_____

_____

_____

_____

_____

_____

_____

_____

_____

_____

Problems - Delays _____

_____

_____

_____

Sub-Contractor Progress _____

_____

_____

_____

Special Assignments _____

_____

_____

Extra Work	Authorized By	Approx. Price

Equipment Rented Today	Rented From	Rate

Supervisor's Signature _____

Weather _____

Temp. AM _____PM _____

Safety Meeting _____

Work Force	No.
Superintendent	_____
Clerk	_____
Bricklayers	_____
Carpenters	_____
Cement Masons	_____
Electricians	_____
Iron Workers	_____
Laborers	_____
Operating Eng.	_____
Plumbers	_____
Pipe Fitters	_____
Sheet Metal	_____
Truck Drivers	_____
Total	_____

Equipment	Hrs.

Material Purchased

DAY _____   DAILY LOG   20___ MAR. 31

CONTRACTOR _____ JOB NAME _____ JOB NO _____

Work Performed Today _____	

Weather _____

Temp. AM _____PM _____

Safety Meeting _____

Work Force	No.
Superintendent	_____
Clerk	_____
Bricklayers	_____
Carpenters	_____
Cement Masons	_____
Electricians	_____
Iron Workers	_____
Laborers	_____
Operating Eng.	_____
Plumbers	_____
Pipe Fitters	_____
Sheet Metal	_____
Truck Drivers	_____
Total	_____

Problems - Delays _____

Equipment	Hrs.

Sub-Contractor Progress _____

Special Assignments _____

Material Purchased	

Extra Work	Authorized By	Approx. Price

Equipment Rented Today	Rented From	Rate

Supervisor's Signature _____

1 APR. 20___   DAILY LOG   DAY _____

CONTRACTOR _____ JOB NAME _____ JOB NO._____

Work Performed Today _____

_____

_____

_____

_____

_____

_____

_____

_____

_____

_____

_____

_____

_____

_____

Problems - Delays _____

_____

_____

_____

Sub-Contractor Progress _____

_____

_____

_____

Special Assignments _____

_____

_____

Weather	_____
Temp. AM _____PM _____	
Safety Meeting _____	

Work Force	No.
Superintendent	_____
Clerk	_____
Bricklayers	_____
Carpenters	_____
Cement Masons	_____
Electricians	_____
Iron Workers	_____
Laborers	_____
Operating Eng.	_____
Plumbers	_____
Pipe Fitters	_____
Sheet Metal	_____
Truck Drivers	_____
Total	_____

Equipment	Hrs.

Material Purchased	

Extra Work	Authorized By	Approx. Price

Equipment Rented Today	Rented From	Rate

Supervisor's Signature _____

DAY _____   DAILY LOG   20___ APR. 2

CONTRACTOR _____ JOB NAME _____ JOB NO _____

Work Performed Today _____		Weather _____
		Temp. AM _____ PM _____
		Safety Meeting _____

Work Force	No.
Superintendent	_____
Clerk	_____
Bricklayers	_____
Carpenters	_____
Cement Masons	_____
Electricians	_____
Iron Workers	_____
Laborers	_____
Operating Eng.	_____
Plumbers	_____
Pipe Fitters	_____
Sheet Metal	_____
Truck Drivers	_____
Total	_____

Problems - Delays _____

Equipment	Hrs.

Sub-Contractor Progress _____

Special Assignments _____

Extra Work	Authorized By	Approx. Price

Equipment Rented Today	Rented From	Rate

Material Purchased

Supervisor's Signature _____

3 APR. 20___   DAILY LOG   DAY _____

CONTRACTOR _____ JOB NAME _____ JOB NO._____

Work Performed Today _____	Weather _____
_____	Temp. AM _____PM _____
_____	Safety Meeting _____

Work Force	**No.**
Superintendent	_____
Clerk	_____
Bricklayers	_____
Carpenters	_____
Cement Masons	_____
Electricians	_____
Iron Workers	_____
Laborers	_____
Operating Eng.	_____
Plumbers	_____
Pipe Fitters	_____
Sheet Metal	_____
Truck Drivers	_____
Total	_____

Problems - Delays _____

Sub-Contractor Progress _____

Equipment	Hrs.

Special Assignments _____

Extra Work	Authorized By	Approx. Price

Equipment Rented Today	Rented From	Rate

Material Purchased

Supervisor's Signature _____

DAY _____   DAILY LOG   20___ APR. 4

CONTRACTOR _____ JOB NAME _____ JOB NO _____

Work Performed Today _____	Weather _____
	Temp. AM _____PM _____
	Safety Meeting _____

Work Force	**No.**
Superintendent	_____
Clerk	_____
Bricklayers	_____
Carpenters	_____
Cement Masons	_____
Electricians	_____
Iron Workers	_____
Laborers	_____
Operating Eng.	_____
Plumbers	_____
Pipe Fitters	_____
Sheet Metal	_____
Truck Drivers	_____
Total	_____

Problems - Delays _____

Equipment	Hrs.

Sub-Contractor Progress _____

Special Assignments _____

Extra Work	Authorized By	Approx. Price

Material Purchased	

Equipment Rented Today	Rented From	Rate

Supervisor's Signature _____

5 APR. 20___   DAILY LOG   DAY _____

CONTRACTOR _____ JOB NAME _____ JOB NO._____

Work Performed Today _____

_____

_____

_____

_____

_____

_____

_____

_____

_____

_____

_____

_____

Problems - Delays _____

_____

_____

_____

Sub-Contractor Progress _____

_____

_____

Special Assignments _____

_____

Weather	_____
Temp. AM _____PM _____	
Safety Meeting _____	

Work Force	No.
Superintendent	_____
Clerk	_____
Bricklayers	_____
Carpenters	_____
Cement Masons	_____
Electricians	_____
Iron Workers	_____
Laborers	_____
Operating Eng.	_____
Plumbers	_____
Pipe Fitters	_____
Sheet Metal	_____
Truck Drivers	_____
Total	_____

Equipment	Hrs.

Extra Work	Authorized By	Approx. Price

Equipment Rented Today	Rented From	Rate

Material Purchased

Supervisor's Signature _____

CONTRACTOR _____ JOB NAME _____ JOB NO _____

Work Performed Today _____	Weather _____
_____	Temp. AM _____PM _____
_____	Safety Meeting _____
_____	**Work Force** **No.**
_____	Superintendent _____
_____	Clerk _____
_____	Bricklayers _____
_____	Carpenters _____
_____	Cement Masons _____
_____	Electricians _____
_____	Iron Workers _____
_____	Laborers _____
_____	Operating Eng. _____
_____	Plumbers _____
_____	Pipe Fitters _____
_____	Sheet Metal _____
	Truck Drivers _____
Problems - Delays _____	
_____	
_____	
_____	
_____	**Total** _____
Sub-Contractor Progress _____	Equipment Hrs.
_____	
_____	
_____	
Special Assignments _____	
_____	
_____	

Extra Work	Authorized By	Approx. Price	Material Purchased

Equipment Rented Today	Rented From	Rate	

Supervisor's Signature _____

7 APR. 20___ DAILY LOG DAY _____

CONTRACTOR _____ JOB NAME _____ JOB NO._____

Work Performed Today _____

_____

_____

_____

_____

_____

_____

_____

_____

_____

_____

Problems - Delays _____

_____

_____

_____

Sub-Contractor Progress _____

_____

_____

_____

Special Assignments _____

_____

_____

Weather _____
Temp. AM _____PM _____
Safety Meeting _____

Work Force	No.
Superintendent	_____
Clerk	_____
Bricklayers	_____
Carpenters	_____
Cement Masons	_____
Electricians	_____
Iron Workers	_____
Laborers	_____
Operating Eng.	_____
Plumbers	_____
Pipe Fitters	_____
Sheet Metal	_____
Truck Drivers	_____
Total	_____

Equipment	Hrs.

Material Purchased	

Extra Work	Authorized By	Approx. Price

Equipment Rented Today	Rented From	Rate

Supervisor's Signature _____

DAY _____   DAILY LOG   20___ APR. 8

CONTRACTOR _____ JOB NAME _____ JOB NO _____

Work Performed Today _____	Weather _____
	Temp. AM _____ PM _____
	Safety Meeting _____

Work Force	**No.**
Superintendent	_____
Clerk	_____
Bricklayers	_____
Carpenters	_____
Cement Masons	_____
Electricians	_____
Iron Workers	_____
Laborers	_____
Operating Eng.	_____
Plumbers	_____
Pipe Fitters	_____
Sheet Metal	_____
Truck Drivers	_____
Total	_____

Problems - Delays _____

Equipment	Hrs.

Sub-Contractor Progress _____

Special Assignments _____

Extra Work	Authorized By	Approx. Price

Material Purchased		

Equipment Rented Today	Rented From	Rate

Supervisor's Signature _____

9 APR. 20___   DAILY LOG   DAY _____

CONTRACTOR _____ JOB NAME _____ JOB NO._____

Work Performed Today _____	Weather _____
	Temp. AM _____PM _____

Work Performed Today _____

_____

_____

_____

_____

_____

_____

_____

_____

_____

_____

_____

_____

_____

Weather _____

Temp. AM _____PM _____

Safety Meeting _____

Work Force	No.
Superintendent	_____
Clerk	_____
Bricklayers	_____
Carpenters	_____
Cement Masons	_____
Electricians	_____
Iron Workers	_____
Laborers	_____
Operating Eng.	_____
Plumbers	_____
Pipe Fitters	_____
Sheet Metal	_____
Truck Drivers	_____
Total	_____

Problems - Delays _____

_____

_____

_____

Sub-Contractor Progress _____

_____

_____

_____

Equipment	Hrs.

Special Assignments _____

_____

_____

_____

Extra Work	Authorized By	Approx. Price

Equipment Rented Today	Rented From	Rate

Material Purchased

Supervisor's Signature _____

DAY _____   DAILY LOG   20___ APR. 10

CONTRACTOR _____ JOB NAME _____ JOB NO _____

Work Performed Today _____	Weather _____
	Temp. AM _____ PM _____

Safety Meeting _____

Work Force	No.
Superintendent	_____
Clerk	_____
Bricklayers	_____
Carpenters	_____
Cement Masons	_____
Electricians	_____
Iron Workers	_____
Laborers	_____
Operating Eng.	_____
Plumbers	_____
Pipe Fitters	_____
Sheet Metal	_____
Truck Drivers	_____
Total	_____

Problems - Delays _____

Equipment	Hrs.

Sub-Contractor Progress _____

Special Assignments _____

Extra Work	Authorized By	Approx. Price

Material Purchased	

Equipment Rented Today	Rented From	Rate

Supervisor's Signature _____

11 APR. 20___   DAILY LOG   DAY _____

CONTRACTOR _____ JOB NAME _____ JOB NO. _____

Work Performed Today _____	Weather _____
_____	Temp. AM _____ PM _____
_____	Safety Meeting _____
_____	

Work Force — No.

Work Force	No.
Superintendent	_____
Clerk	_____
Bricklayers	_____
Carpenters	_____
Cement Masons	_____
Electricians	_____
Iron Workers	_____
Laborers	_____
Operating Eng.	_____
Plumbers	_____
Pipe Fitters	_____
Sheet Metal	_____
Truck Drivers	_____
Total	_____

Problems - Delays _____
_____
_____
_____

Sub-Contractor Progress _____
_____
_____
_____

Special Assignments _____
_____
_____

Equipment	Hrs.

Extra Work	Authorized By	Approx. Price

Equipment Rented Today	Rented From	Rate

Material Purchased

Supervisor's Signature _____

DAY _____   DAILY LOG   20___ APR. 12

CONTRACTOR _____ JOB NAME _____ JOB NO _____

Work Performed Today _____	Weather _____
	Temp. AM _____ PM _____
	Safety Meeting _____

Work Force	No.
Superintendent	_____
Clerk	_____
Bricklayers	_____
Carpenters	_____
Cement Masons	_____
Electricians	_____
Iron Workers	_____
Laborers	_____
Operating Eng.	_____
Plumbers	_____
Pipe Fitters	_____
Sheet Metal	_____
Truck Drivers	_____
Total	_____

Problems - Delays _____

Equipment	Hrs.

Sub-Contractor Progress _____

Special Assignments _____

Extra Work	Authorized By	Approx. Price

Material Purchased		

Equipment Rented Today	Rented From	Rate

Supervisor's Signature _____

13 APR. 20___   DAILY LOG   DAY _____

CONTRACTOR _____ JOB NAME _____ JOB NO._____

Work Performed Today _____	Weather _____
_____	Temp. AM _____PM _____
_____	Safety Meeting _____

Work Force	No.
Superintendent	_____
Clerk	_____
Bricklayers	_____
Carpenters	_____
Cement Masons	_____
Electricians	_____
Iron Workers	_____
Laborers	_____
Operating Eng.	_____
Plumbers	_____
Pipe Fitters	_____
Sheet Metal	_____
Truck Drivers	_____
Total	_____

Problems - Delays _____

Sub-Contractor Progress _____

Equipment	Hrs.

Special Assignments _____

Extra Work	Authorized By	Approx. Price

Equipment Rented Today	Rented From	Rate

Material Purchased

Supervisor's Signature _____

DAY _____   DAILY LOG   20___ APR. 14

CONTRACTOR _____ JOB NAME _____ JOB NO _____

Work Performed Today _____	Weather _____
_____	Temp. AM _____PM _____
_____	
_____	Safety Meeting _____

Work Force	No.
Superintendent	_____
Clerk	_____
Bricklayers	_____
Carpenters	_____
Cement Masons	_____
Electricians	_____
Iron Workers	_____
Laborers	_____
Operating Eng.	_____
Plumbers	_____
Pipe Fitters	_____
Sheet Metal	_____
Truck Drivers	_____
Total	_____

Problems - Delays _____

Sub-Contractor Progress _____

Equipment	Hrs.

Special Assignments _____

Extra Work	Authorized By	Approx. Price

Equipment Rented Today	Rented From	Rate

Material Purchased

Supervisor's Signature _____

15 APR. 20___   DAILY LOG   DAY _____

CONTRACTOR _____ JOB NAME _____ JOB NO._____

Work Performed Today _____	Weather _____

Temp. AM _____ PM _____

Safety Meeting _____

Work Force	No.
Superintendent	_____
Clerk	_____
Bricklayers	_____
Carpenters	_____
Cement Masons	_____
Electricians	_____
Iron Workers	_____
Laborers	_____
Operating Eng.	_____
Plumbers	_____
Pipe Fitters	_____
Sheet Metal	_____
Truck Drivers	_____
Total	_____

Problems - Delays _____

Equipment	Hrs.

Sub-Contractor Progress _____

Special Assignments _____

Extra Work	Authorized By	Approx. Price

Material Purchased

Equipment Rented Today	Rented From	Rate

Supervisor's Signature _____

DAY _____   DAILY LOG   20___ APR. 16

CONTRACTOR _____ JOB NAME _____ JOB NO _____

Work Performed Today _____	Weather _____
	Temp. AM _____ PM _____

Work Performed Today _____

_____

_____

_____

_____

_____

_____

_____

_____

_____

_____

_____

_____

Weather _____

Temp. AM _____ PM _____

Safety Meeting _____

Work Force	No.
Superintendent	_____
Clerk	_____
Bricklayers	_____
Carpenters	_____
Cement Masons	_____
Electricians	_____
Iron Workers	_____
Laborers	_____
Operating Eng.	_____
Plumbers	_____
Pipe Fitters	_____
Sheet Metal	_____
Truck Drivers	_____
Total	_____

Problems - Delays _____

_____

_____

_____

_____

Sub-Contractor Progress _____

_____

_____

_____

Equipment	Hrs.

Special Assignments _____

_____

_____

_____

Extra Work	Authorized By	Approx. Price

Equipment Rented Today	Rented From	Rate

Material Purchased

Supervisor's Signature _____

17 APR. 20___   DAILY LOG   DAY _____

CONTRACTOR _____ JOB NAME _____ JOB NO._____

Work Performed Today _____

_____

_____

_____

_____

_____

_____

_____

_____

_____

_____

_____

_____

_____

_____

Problems - Delays _____

_____

_____

_____

Sub-Contractor Progress _____

_____

_____

_____

Special Assignments _____

_____

_____

| Weather _____ |
| Temp. AM _____PM _____ |
| Safety Meeting _____ |

Work Force	No.
Superintendent	_____
Clerk	_____
Bricklayers	_____
Carpenters	_____
Cement Masons	_____
Electricians	_____
Iron Workers	_____
Laborers	_____
Operating Eng.	_____
Plumbers	_____
Pipe Fitters	_____
Sheet Metal	_____
Truck Drivers	_____
Total	_____

Equipment	Hrs.

Extra Work	Authorized By	Approx. Price

Equipment Rented Today	Rented From	Rate

Material Purchased

Supervisor's Signature _____

DAY _____   DAILY LOG   20___ APR. 18

CONTRACTOR _____ JOB NAME _____ JOB NO _____

Work Performed Today _____

_____

_____

_____

_____

_____

_____

_____

_____

_____

_____

_____

_____

_____

_____

_____

Problems - Delays _____

_____

_____

_____

Sub-Contractor Progress _____

_____

_____

_____

Special Assignments _____

_____

_____

| Weather | _____ |

Temp. AM _____ PM _____

Safety Meeting _____

Work Force	No.
Superintendent	_____
Clerk	_____
Bricklayers	_____
Carpenters	_____
Cement Masons	_____
Electricians	_____
Iron Workers	_____
Laborers	_____
Operating Eng.	_____
Plumbers	_____
Pipe Fitters	_____
Sheet Metal	_____
Truck Drivers	_____
Total	_____

Equipment	Hrs.

Extra Work	Authorized By	Approx. Price

Equipment Rented Today	Rented From	Rate

Material Purchased

Supervisor's Signature _____

19 APR. 20____   DAILY LOG   DAY _____

CONTRACTOR _____ JOB NAME _____ JOB NO._____

Work Performed Today _____

_____

_____

_____

_____

_____

_____

_____

_____

_____

_____

_____

_____

Problems - Delays _____

_____

_____

_____

Sub-Contractor Progress _____

_____

_____

_____

Special Assignments _____

_____

_____

Weather	_____
Temp. AM _____ PM _____	
Safety Meeting _____	

Work Force	No.
Superintendent	_____
Clerk	_____
Bricklayers	_____
Carpenters	_____
Cement Masons	_____
Electricians	_____
Iron Workers	_____
Laborers	_____
Operating Eng.	_____
Plumbers	_____
Pipe Fitters	_____
Sheet Metal	_____
Truck Drivers	_____
Total	_____

Equipment	Hrs.

Extra Work	Authorized By	Approx. Price

Equipment Rented Today	Rented From	Rate

Material Purchased

Supervisor's Signature _____

DAY _____   DAILY LOG   20___ APR. 20

CONTRACTOR _____ JOB NAME _____ JOB NO _____

Work Performed Today _____	Weather _____
	Temp. AM _____PM _____
	Safety Meeting _____

Work Force	No.
Superintendent	_____
Clerk	_____
Bricklayers	_____
Carpenters	_____
Cement Masons	_____
Electricians	_____
Iron Workers	_____
Laborers	_____
Operating Eng.	_____
Plumbers	_____
Pipe Fitters	_____
Sheet Metal	_____
Truck Drivers	_____
Total	_____

Problems - Delays _____

Equipment	Hrs.

Sub-Contractor Progress _____

Special Assignments _____

Extra Work	Authorized By	Approx. Price

Equipment Rented Today	Rented From	Rate

Material Purchased

Supervisor's Signature _____

21 APR. 20___   DAILY LOG   DAY _____

CONTRACTOR _____ JOB NAME _____ JOB NO._____

Work Performed Today _____

_____

_____

_____

_____

_____

_____

_____

_____

_____

_____

_____

_____

Problems - Delays _____

_____

_____

_____

Sub-Contractor Progress _____

_____

_____

_____

Special Assignments _____

_____

_____

Weather	_____
Temp. AM _____ PM _____	
Safety Meeting _____	

Work Force	No.
Superintendent	_____
Clerk	_____
Bricklayers	_____
Carpenters	_____
Cement Masons	_____
Electricians	_____
Iron Workers	_____
Laborers	_____
Operating Eng.	_____
Plumbers	_____
Pipe Fitters	_____
Sheet Metal	_____
Truck Drivers	_____
Total	_____

Equipment	Hrs.

Material Purchased

Extra Work	Authorized By	Approx. Price

Equipment Rented Today	Rented From	Rate

Supervisor's Signature _____

DAY _____   DAILY LOG   20___ APR. 22

CONTRACTOR _____ JOB NAME _____ JOB NO _____

Work Performed Today _____		

Work Performed Today _____

_____

_____

_____

_____

_____

_____

_____

_____

_____

_____

_____

_____

_____

Problems - Delays _____

_____

_____

_____

Sub-Contractor Progress _____

_____

_____

Special Assignments _____

_____

_____

Weather _____

Temp. AM _____ PM _____

Safety Meeting _____

Work Force	No.
Superintendent	_____
Clerk	_____
Bricklayers	_____
Carpenters	_____
Cement Masons	_____
Electricians	_____
Iron Workers	_____
Laborers	_____
Operating Eng.	_____
Plumbers	_____
Pipe Fitters	_____
Sheet Metal	_____
Truck Drivers	_____
Total	_____

Equipment	Hrs.

Extra Work	Authorized By	Approx. Price

Equipment Rented Today	Rented From	Rate

Material Purchased

Supervisor's Signature _____

23 APR. 20___   DAILY LOG   DAY _____

CONTRACTOR _____ JOB NAME _____ JOB NO._____

Work Performed Today _____

_____

_____

_____

_____

_____

_____

_____

_____

_____

_____

_____

_____

Problems - Delays _____

_____

_____

_____

Sub-Contractor Progress _____

_____

_____

_____

Special Assignments _____

_____

_____

Weather	_____
Temp. AM _____ PM _____	
Safety Meeting _____	

Work Force	No.
Superintendent	_____
Clerk	_____
Bricklayers	_____
Carpenters	_____
Cement Masons	_____
Electricians	_____
Iron Workers	_____
Laborers	_____
Operating Eng.	_____
Plumbers	_____
Pipe Fitters	_____
Sheet Metal	_____
Truck Drivers	_____
Total	_____

Equipment	Hrs.

Material Purchased	

Extra Work	Authorized By	Approx. Price

Equipment Rented Today	Rented From	Rate

Supervisor's Signature _____

DAY _____   DAILY LOG   20___ APR. 24

CONTRACTOR _____ JOB NAME _____ JOB NO _____

Work Performed Today _____	Weather _____
	Temp. AM _____ PM _____
	Safety Meeting _____

Work Force	No.
Superintendent	_____
Clerk	_____
Bricklayers	_____
Carpenters	_____
Cement Masons	_____
Electricians	_____
Iron Workers	_____
Laborers	_____
Operating Eng.	_____
Plumbers	_____
Pipe Fitters	_____
Sheet Metal	_____
Truck Drivers	_____
Total	_____

Problems - Delays _____

Equipment	Hrs.

Sub-Contractor Progress _____

Special Assignments _____

Extra Work	Authorized By	Approx. Price

Material Purchased

Equipment Rented Today	Rented From	Rate

Supervisor's Signature _____

25 APR. 20___   DAILY LOG   DAY _____

CONTRACTOR _____ JOB NAME _____ JOB NO._____

Work Performed Today _____	Weather _____
	Temp. AM _____PM _____
	Safety Meeting _____

Work Force	No.
Superintendent	_____
Clerk	_____
Bricklayers	_____
Carpenters	_____
Cement Masons	_____
Electricians	_____
Iron Workers	_____
Laborers	_____
Operating Eng.	_____
Plumbers	_____
Pipe Fitters	_____
Sheet Metal	_____
Truck Drivers	_____
Total	_____

Problems - Delays _____

Sub-Contractor Progress _____

Special Assignments _____

Equipment	Hrs.

Extra Work	Authorized By	Approx. Price

Equipment Rented Today	Rented From	Rate

Material Purchased

Supervisor's Signature _____

DAY _____   DAILY LOG   20 ___ APR. 26

CONTRACTOR _____ JOB NAME _____ JOB NO _____

Work Performed Today _____	Weather _____
_____	Temp. AM _____ PM _____
_____	Safety Meeting _____

Work Force	No.
Superintendent	_____
Clerk	_____
Bricklayers	_____
Carpenters	_____
Cement Masons	_____
Electricians	_____
Iron Workers	_____
Laborers	_____
Operating Eng.	_____
Plumbers	_____
Pipe Fitters	_____
Sheet Metal	_____
Truck Drivers	_____
Total	_____

Problems - Delays _____

Sub-Contractor Progress _____

Equipment	Hrs.

Special Assignments _____

Extra Work	Authorized By	Approx. Price

Equipment Rented Today	Rented From	Rate

Material Purchased

Supervisor's Signature _____

27 APR. 20___   DAILY LOG   DAY _____

CONTRACTOR _____ JOB NAME _____ JOB NO._____

Work Performed Today _____

_____

_____

_____

_____

_____

_____

_____

_____

_____

_____

_____

_____

_____

Problems - Delays _____

_____

_____

_____

Sub-Contractor Progress _____

_____

_____

_____

Special Assignments _____

_____

_____

_____

Weather	_____
Temp. AM _____ PM _____	
Safety Meeting _____	

Work Force	No.
Superintendent	_____
Clerk	_____
Bricklayers	_____
Carpenters	_____
Cement Masons	_____
Electricians	_____
Iron Workers	_____
Laborers	_____
Operating Eng.	_____
Plumbers	_____
Pipe Fitters	_____
Sheet Metal	_____
Truck Drivers	_____
Total	_____

Equipment	Hrs.

Extra Work	Authorized By	Approx. Price

Equipment Rented Today	Rented From	Rate

Material Purchased

Supervisor's Signature _____

DAY _____   DAILY LOG   20___ APR. 28

CONTRACTOR _____ JOB NAME _____ JOB NO _____

Work Performed Today _____	Weather _____
	Temp. AM _____PM _____
	Safety Meeting _____

Work Force	No.
Superintendent	_____
Clerk	_____
Bricklayers	_____
Carpenters	_____
Cement Masons	_____
Electricians	_____
Iron Workers	_____
Laborers	_____
Operating Eng.	_____
Plumbers	_____
Pipe Fitters	_____
Sheet Metal	
Truck Drivers	_____
Total	_____

Problems - Delays _____

Equipment	Hrs.

Sub-Contractor Progress _____

Special Assignments _____

Extra Work	Authorized By	Approx. Price

Equipment Rented Today	Rented From	Rate

Material Purchased

Supervisor's Signature _____

29 APR. 20____   DAILY LOG   DAY _____

CONTRACTOR _____ JOB NAME _____ JOB NO._____

Work Performed Today _____	Weather _____
	Temp. AM _____PM _____
_____	Safety Meeting _____

Work Force	No.
Superintendent	_____
Clerk	_____
Bricklayers	_____
Carpenters	_____
Cement Masons	_____
Electricians	_____
Iron Workers	_____
Laborers	_____
Operating Eng.	_____
Plumbers	_____
Pipe Fitters	_____
Sheet Metal	_____
Truck Drivers	_____
Total	_____

Problems - Delays _____

Sub-Contractor Progress _____

Equipment	Hrs.

Special Assignments _____

Extra Work	Authorized By	Approx. Price

Equipment Rented Today	Rented From	Rate

Material Purchased

Supervisor's Signature _____

DAY _____   DAILY LOG   20___   APR. 30

CONTRACTOR _____ JOB NAME _____ JOB NO _____

Work Performed Today _____	Weather _____
_____	Temp. AM _____PM _____
_____	Safety Meeting _____
_____	

Work Force	No.
Superintendent	_____
Clerk	_____
Bricklayers	_____
Carpenters	_____
Cement Masons	_____
Electricians	_____
Iron Workers	_____
Laborers	_____
Operating Eng.	_____
Plumbers	_____
Pipe Fitters	_____
Sheet Metal	_____
Truck Drivers	_____
Total	_____

Problems - Delays _____

Equipment	Hrs.

Sub-Contractor Progress _____

Special Assignments _____

Extra Work	Authorized By	Approx. Price

Material Purchased		

Equipment Rented Today	Rented From	Rate

Supervisor's Signature _____

1 MAY 20___   DAILY LOG   DAY _____

CONTRACTOR _____ JOB NAME _____ JOB NO._____

Work Performed Today _____	Weather _____
	Temp. AM _____PM _____
	Safety Meeting _____

Work Force	No.
Superintendent	_____
Clerk	_____
Bricklayers	_____
Carpenters	_____
Cement Masons	_____
Electricians	_____
Iron Workers	_____
Laborers	_____
Operating Eng.	_____
Plumbers	_____
Pipe Fitters	_____
Sheet Metal	_____
Truck Drivers	_____
Total	_____

Problems - Delays _____

Sub-Contractor Progress _____

Equipment	Hrs.

Special Assignments _____

Extra Work	Authorized By	Approx. Price

Equipment Rented Today	Rented From	Rate

Material Purchased

Supervisor's Signature _____

DAY _____   DAILY LOG   20___ MAY 2

CONTRACTOR _____ JOB NAME _____ JOB NO _____

Work Performed Today _____	Weather _____
	Temp. AM _____PM _____
	Safety Meeting _____

Work Force	No.
Superintendent	_____
Clerk	_____
Bricklayers	_____
Carpenters	_____
Cement Masons	_____
Electricians	_____
Iron Workers	_____
Laborers	_____
Operating Eng.	_____
Plumbers	_____
Pipe Fitters	_____
Sheet Metal	_____
Truck Drivers	_____
Total	_____

Problems - Delays _____

Equipment	Hrs.

Sub-Contractor Progress _____

Special Assignments _____

Extra Work	Authorized By	Approx. Price

Material Purchased

Equipment Rented Today	Rented From	Rate

Supervisor's Signature _____

3 MAY 20___   DAILY LOG   DAY _____

CONTRACTOR _____ JOB NAME _____ JOB NO._____

Work Performed Today _____	Weather _____
_____	Temp. AM _____PM _____
_____	Safety Meeting _____
_____	

Work Force	No.
Superintendent	_____
Clerk	_____
Bricklayers	_____
Carpenters	_____
Cement Masons	_____
Electricians	_____
Iron Workers	_____
Laborers	_____
Operating Eng.	_____
Plumbers	_____
Pipe Fitters	_____
Sheet Metal	_____
Truck Drivers	_____
Total	_____

Problems - Delays _____

Equipment	Hrs.

Sub-Contractor Progress _____

Special Assignments _____

Extra Work	Authorized By	Approx. Price

Equipment Rented Today	Rented From	Rate

Material Purchased

Supervisor's Signature _____

DAY _____   DAILY LOG   20___   MAY 4

CONTRACTOR _____ JOB NAME _____ JOB NO _____

Work Performed Today _____	Weather _____
_____	Temp. AM _____ PM _____
_____	Safety Meeting _____

Work Force	No.
Superintendent	_____
Clerk	_____
Bricklayers	_____
Carpenters	_____
Cement Masons	_____
Electricians	_____
Iron Workers	_____
Laborers	_____
Operating Eng.	_____
Plumbers	_____
Pipe Fitters	_____
Sheet Metal	_____
Truck Drivers	_____
Total	_____

Problems - Delays _____

Sub-Contractor Progress _____

Special Assignments _____

Equipment	Hrs.

Extra Work	Authorized By	Approx. Price

Equipment Rented Today	Rented From	Rate

Material Purchased

Supervisor's Signature _____

5 MAY 20___ DAILY LOG DAY _____

CONTRACTOR _____ JOB NAME _____ JOB NO._____

Work Performed Today _____	Weather _____
	Temp. AM _____PM _____
	Safety Meeting _____

Work Force	No.
Superintendent	_____
Clerk	_____
Bricklayers	_____
Carpenters	_____
Cement Masons	_____
Electricians	_____
Iron Workers	_____
Laborers	_____
Operating Eng.	_____
Plumbers	_____
Pipe Fitters	_____
Sheet Metal	_____
Truck Drivers	_____
Total	_____

Problems - Delays _____

Sub-Contractor Progress _____

Special Assignments _____

Equipment	Hrs.

Extra Work	Authorized By	Approx. Price

Equipment Rented Today	Rented From	Rate

Material Purchased

Supervisor's Signature _____

DAY _____   DAILY LOG   20___ MAY 6

CONTRACTOR _____ JOB NAME _____ JOB NO _____

| Work Performed Today _____ | Weather _____ |
| | Temp. AM _____PM _____ |

Safety Meeting _____

Work Force	No.
Superintendent	_____
Clerk	_____
Bricklayers	_____
Carpenters	_____
Cement Masons	_____
Electricians	_____
Iron Workers	_____
Laborers	_____
Operating Eng.	_____
Plumbers	_____
Pipe Fitters	_____
Sheet Metal	_____
Truck Drivers	_____
Total	_____

Problems - Delays _____

Equipment	Hrs.

Sub-Contractor Progress _____

Special Assignments _____

Extra Work	Authorized By	Approx. Price

Equipment Rented Today	Rented From	Rate

Material Purchased

Supervisor's Signature _____

7 MAY 20___   DAILY LOG   DAY _____

CONTRACTOR _____ JOB NAME _____ JOB NO. _____

Work Performed Today _____

_____

_____

_____

_____

_____

_____

_____

_____

_____

_____

_____

_____

_____

Problems - Delays _____

_____

_____

_____

Sub-Contractor Progress _____

_____

_____

_____

Special Assignments _____

_____

_____

| Weather _____ |
| Temp. AM _____PM _____ |

Safety Meeting _____

Work Force	No.
Superintendent	_____
Clerk	_____
Bricklayers	_____
Carpenters	_____
Cement Masons	_____
Electricians	_____
Iron Workers	_____
Laborers	_____
Operating Eng.	_____
Plumbers	_____
Pipe Fitters	_____
Sheet Metal	_____
Truck Drivers	_____
Total	_____

Equipment	Hrs.

Extra Work	Authorized By	Approx. Price

Equipment Rented Today	Rented From	Rate

Material Purchased

Supervisor's Signature _____

DAY _____   DAILY LOG   20___ MAY 8

CONTRACTOR _____ JOB NAME _____ JOB NO _____

Work Performed Today _____

_____

_____

_____

_____

_____

_____

_____

_____

_____

_____

_____

_____

_____

Problems - Delays _____

_____

_____

_____

_____

Sub-Contractor Progress _____

_____

_____

_____

Special Assignments _____

_____

_____

Extra Work	Authorized By	Approx. Price

Equipment Rented Today	Rented From	Rate

Supervisor's Signature _____

Weather _____

Temp. AM _____ PM _____

Safety Meeting _____

Work Force	No.
Superintendent	_____
Clerk	_____
Bricklayers	_____
Carpenters	_____
Cement Masons	_____
Electricians	_____
Iron Workers	_____
Laborers	_____
Operating Eng.	_____
Plumbers	_____
Pipe Fitters	_____
Sheet Metal	_____
Truck Drivers	_____
Total	_____

Equipment	Hrs.

Material Purchased

9 MAY 20___   DAILY LOG   DAY _____

CONTRACTOR _____ JOB NAME _____ JOB NO._____

Work Performed Today _____

_____

_____

_____

_____

_____

_____

_____

_____

_____

_____

_____

_____

Problems - Delays _____

_____

_____

_____

_____

Sub-Contractor Progress _____

_____

_____

_____

Special Assignments _____

_____

_____

Extra Work	Authorized By	Approx. Price

Equipment Rented Today	Rented From	Rate

Supervisor's Signature _____

Weather _____

Temp. AM _____PM _____

Safety Meeting _____

Work Force	No.
Superintendent	_____
Clerk	_____
Bricklayers	_____
Carpenters	_____
Cement Masons	_____
Electricians	_____
Iron Workers	_____
Laborers	_____
Operating Eng.	_____
Plumbers	_____
Pipe Fitters	_____
Sheet Metal	_____
Truck Drivers	_____
Total	_____

Equipment	Hrs.

Material Purchased

DAY _____   DAILY LOG   20___ MAY 10

CONTRACTOR _____ JOB NAME _____ JOB NO _____

Work Performed Today _____	Weather _____
_____	Temp. AM _____ PM _____
_____	Safety Meeting _____

Work Force	No.
Superintendent	_____
Clerk	_____
Bricklayers	_____
Carpenters	_____
Cement Masons	_____
Electricians	_____
Iron Workers	_____
Laborers	_____
Operating Eng.	_____
Plumbers	_____
Pipe Fitters	_____
Sheet Metal	_____
Truck Drivers	_____
Total	_____

Problems - Delays _____
_____
_____
_____

Equipment	Hrs.

Sub-Contractor Progress _____
_____
_____
_____

Special Assignments _____
_____
_____

Extra Work	Authorized By	Approx. Price

Equipment Rented Today	Rented From	Rate

Material Purchased

Supervisor's Signature _____

11 MAY 20___   DAILY LOG   DAY _____

CONTRACTOR _____ JOB NAME _____ JOB NO._____

Work Performed Today _____	Weather _____
_____	Temp. AM _____PM _____
_____	Safety Meeting _____

	Work Force	**No.**
	Superintendent	_____
	Clerk	_____
	Bricklayers	_____
	Carpenters	_____
	Cement Masons	_____
	Electricians	_____
	Iron Workers	_____
	Laborers	_____
	Operating Eng.	_____
	Plumbers	_____
	Pipe Fitters	_____
	Sheet Metal	_____
	Truck Drivers	_____

Work Performed Today (continued)
_____
_____
_____
_____
_____
_____

Problems - Delays _____
_____
_____
_____

| **Total** | _____ |

Sub-Contractor Progress _____

Equipment	Hrs.

Special Assignments _____
_____
_____

Extra Work	Authorized By	Approx. Price

Material Purchased	

Equipment Rented Today	Rented From	Rate

Supervisor's Signature _____

DAY _____   DAILY LOG   20___ MAY 12

CONTRACTOR _____ JOB NAME _____ JOB NO _____

Work Performed Today _____

_____

_____

_____

_____

_____

_____

_____

_____

_____

_____

_____

_____

_____

Problems - Delays _____

_____

_____

_____

Sub-Contractor Progress _____

_____

_____

_____

Special Assignments _____

_____

_____

| Weather _____ |
| Temp. AM _____ PM _____ |
| Safety Meeting _____ |

Work Force	No.
Superintendent	_____
Clerk	_____
Bricklayers	_____
Carpenters	_____
Cement Masons	_____
Electricians	_____
Iron Workers	_____
Laborers	_____
Operating Eng.	_____
Plumbers	_____
Pipe Fitters	_____
Sheet Metal	_____
Truck Drivers	_____
Total	_____

Equipment	Hrs.

Extra Work	Authorized By	Approx. Price

Equipment Rented Today	Rented From	Rate

Material Purchased

Supervisor's Signature _____

13 MAY 20____   DAILY LOG   DAY _____

CONTRACTOR _____ JOB NAME _____ JOB NO._____

| Work Performed Today _____ | Weather _____ |

Temp. AM _____PM _____

Safety Meeting _____

Work Force	**No.**
Superintendent	_____
Clerk	_____
Bricklayers	_____
Carpenters	_____
Cement Masons	_____
Electricians	_____
Iron Workers	_____
Laborers	_____
Operating Eng.	_____
Plumbers	_____
Pipe Fitters	_____
Sheet Metal	_____
Truck Drivers	_____
Total	_____

Problems - Delays _____

Equipment	Hrs.

Sub-Contractor Progress _____

Special Assignments _____

Material Purchased	

Extra Work	Authorized By	Approx. Price

Equipment Rented Today	Rented From	Rate

Supervisor's Signature _____

DAY _____   DAILY LOG   20___ MAY 14

CONTRACTOR _____ JOB NAME _____ JOB NO _____

Work Performed Today _____	Weather _____
	Temp. AM _____ PM _____
	Safety Meeting _____

Work Force	**No.**
Superintendent	_____
Clerk	_____
Bricklayers	_____
Carpenters	_____
Cement Masons	_____
Electricians	_____
Iron Workers	_____
Laborers	_____
Operating Eng.	_____
Plumbers	_____
Pipe Fitters	_____
Sheet Metal	_____
Truck Drivers	_____
Total	_____

Problems - Delays _____

Equipment	Hrs.

Sub-Contractor Progress _____

Special Assignments _____

Extra Work	Authorized By	Approx. Price

Material Purchased	

Equipment Rented Today	Rented From	Rate

Supervisor's Signature _____

15 MAY 20___   DAILY LOG   DAY _____

CONTRACTOR _____ JOB NAME _____ JOB NO._____

Work Performed Today _____

_____

_____

_____

_____

_____

_____

_____

_____

_____

_____

_____

_____

_____

Problems - Delays _____

_____

_____

_____

Sub-Contractor Progress _____

_____

_____

_____

Special Assignments _____

_____

_____

Extra Work	Authorized By	Approx. Price

Equipment Rented Today	Rented From	Rate

Supervisor's Signature _____

Weather _____

Temp. AM _____PM _____

Safety Meeting _____

Work Force	No.
Superintendent	_____
Clerk	_____
Bricklayers	_____
Carpenters	_____
Cement Masons	_____
Electricians	_____
Iron Workers	_____
Laborers	_____
Operating Eng.	_____
Plumbers	_____
Pipe Fitters	_____
Sheet Metal	_____
Truck Drivers	_____
Total	_____

Equipment	Hrs.

Material Purchased	

DAY _____   DAILY LOG   20___ MAY 16

CONTRACTOR _____ JOB NAME _____ JOB NO _____

Work Performed Today _____

_____

_____

_____

_____

_____

_____

_____

_____

_____

_____

_____

_____

Problems - Delays _____

_____

_____

_____

Sub-Contractor Progress _____

_____

_____

Special Assignments _____

_____

_____

Extra Work	Authorized By	Approx. Price

Equipment Rented Today	Rented From	Rate

Supervisor's Signature _____

Weather _____

Temp. AM _____PM _____

Safety Meeting _____

Work Force	No.
Superintendent	_____
Clerk	_____
Bricklayers	_____
Carpenters	_____
Cement Masons	_____
Electricians	_____
Iron Workers	_____
Laborers	_____
Operating Eng.	_____
Plumbers	_____
Pipe Fitters	_____
Sheet Metal	_____
Truck Drivers	_____
Total	_____

Equipment	Hrs.

Material Purchased

17 MAY 20___   DAILY LOG   DAY _____

CONTRACTOR _____ JOB NAME _____ JOB NO._____

Work Performed Today _____

_____

_____

_____

_____

_____

_____

_____

_____

_____

_____

_____

Problems - Delays _____

_____

_____

_____

Sub-Contractor Progress _____

_____

_____

_____

Special Assignments _____

_____

_____

Extra Work	Authorized By	Approx. Price

Equipment Rented Today	Rented From	Rate

Supervisor's Signature _____

Weather _____

Temp. AM _____ PM _____

Safety Meeting _____

Work Force	No.
Superintendent	_____
Clerk	_____
Bricklayers	_____
Carpenters	_____
Cement Masons	_____
Electricians	_____
Iron Workers	_____
Laborers	_____
Operating Eng.	_____
Plumbers	_____
Pipe Fitters	_____
Sheet Metal	_____
Truck Drivers	_____
Total	_____

Equipment	Hrs.

Material Purchased

DAY _____   DAILY LOG   20___ MAY 18

CONTRACTOR _____ JOB NAME _____ JOB NO _____

Work Performed Today _____	Weather _____
_____	Temp. AM _____ PM _____
_____	
_____	Safety Meeting _____
_____	

Work Force	No.
Superintendent	_____
Clerk	_____
Bricklayers	_____
Carpenters	_____
Cement Masons	_____
Electricians	_____
Iron Workers	_____
Laborers	_____
Operating Eng.	_____
Plumbers	_____
Pipe Fitters	_____
Sheet Metal	_____
Truck Drivers	_____
Total	_____

Problems - Delays _____
_____
_____
_____
_____

Sub-Contractor Progress _____
_____
_____
_____

Equipment	Hrs.

Special Assignments _____
_____
_____

Extra Work	Authorized By	Approx. Price

Equipment Rented Today	Rented From	Rate

Material Purchased

Supervisor's Signature _____

19 MAY 20____   DAILY LOG   DAY _____

CONTRACTOR _____ JOB NAME _____ JOB NO._____

Work Performed Today _____	Weather _____
_____	Temp. AM _____PM _____
_____	Safety Meeting _____

Work Force	No.
Superintendent	_____
Clerk	_____
Bricklayers	_____
Carpenters	_____
Cement Masons	_____
Electricians	_____
Iron Workers	_____
Laborers	_____
Operating Eng.	_____
Plumbers	_____
Pipe Fitters	_____
Sheet Metal	_____
Truck Drivers	_____
Total	_____

Problems - Delays _____

Sub-Contractor Progress _____

Special Assignments _____

Equipment	Hrs.

Extra Work	Authorized By	Approx. Price

Equipment Rented Today	Rented From	Rate

Material Purchased

Supervisor's Signature _____

DAY _____   DAILY LOG   20___ MAY 20

CONTRACTOR _____ JOB NAME _____ JOB NO _____

Work Performed Today _____

_____

_____

_____

_____

_____

_____

_____

_____

_____

_____

_____

_____

Problems - Delays _____

_____

_____

_____

Sub-Contractor Progress _____

_____

_____

_____

Special Assignments _____

_____

_____

Extra Work	Authorized By	Approx. Price

Equipment Rented Today	Rented From	Rate

Supervisor's Signature _____

Weather	
Temp. AM _____ PM _____	
Safety Meeting _____	

Work Force	No.
Superintendent	_____
Clerk	_____
Bricklayers	_____
Carpenters	_____
Cement Masons	_____
Electricians	_____
Iron Workers	_____
Laborers	_____
Operating Eng.	_____
Plumbers	_____
Pipe Fitters	_____
Sheet Metal	_____
Truck Drivers	_____
Total	_____

Equipment	Hrs.

Material Purchased

21 MAY 20___   DAILY LOG   DAY _____

CONTRACTOR _____ JOB NAME _____ JOB NO._____

Work Performed Today _____

_____

_____

_____

_____

_____

_____

_____

_____

_____

_____

_____

_____

_____

Problems - Delays _____

_____

_____

_____

_____

Sub-Contractor Progress _____

_____

_____

_____

Special Assignments _____

_____

_____

Extra Work	Authorized By	Approx. Price

Equipment Rented Today	Rented From	Rate

Supervisor's Signature _____

Weather _____

Temp. AM _____PM _____

Safety Meeting _____

Work Force	No.
Superintendent	_____
Clerk	_____
Bricklayers	_____
Carpenters	_____
Cement Masons	_____
Electricians	_____
Iron Workers	_____
Laborers	_____
Operating Eng.	_____
Plumbers	_____
Pipe Fitters	_____
Sheet Metal	_____
Truck Drivers	_____
Total	_____

Equipment	Hrs.

Material Purchased

DAY _____   DAILY LOG   20___ MAY 22

CONTRACTOR _____ JOB NAME _____ JOB NO _____

Work Performed Today _____

_____

_____

_____

_____

_____

_____

_____

_____

_____

_____

_____

_____

_____

Problems - Delays _____

_____

_____

_____

Sub-Contractor Progress _____

_____

_____

_____

Special Assignments _____

_____

_____

Weather	
Temp. AM _____ PM _____	
Safety Meeting _____	

Work Force	No.
Superintendent	_____
Clerk	_____
Bricklayers	_____
Carpenters	_____
Cement Masons	_____
Electricians	_____
Iron Workers	_____
Laborers	_____
Operating Eng.	_____
Plumbers	_____
Pipe Fitters	_____
Sheet Metal	_____
Truck Drivers	_____
Total	_____

Equipment	Hrs.

Extra Work	Authorized By	Approx. Price

Equipment Rented Today	Rented From	Rate

Material Purchased	

Supervisor's Signature _____

23 MAY 20____   DAILY LOG   DAY _____

CONTRACTOR _____ JOB NAME _____ JOB NO._____

Work Performed Today _____ _____ _____ _____ _____ _____ _____ _____ _____ _____ _____ _____ _____ _____	Weather _____ Temp. AM _____PM _____ Safety Meeting _____

Work Force	No.
Superintendent	_____
Clerk	_____
Bricklayers	_____
Carpenters	_____
Cement Masons	_____
Electricians	_____
Iron Workers	_____
Laborers	_____
Operating Eng.	_____
Plumbers	_____
Pipe Fitters	_____
Sheet Metal	_____
Truck Drivers	_____
Total	_____

Problems - Delays _____

_____

_____

_____

Equipment	Hrs.

Sub-Contractor Progress _____

_____

_____

_____

Special Assignments _____

_____

_____

Material Purchased

Extra Work	Authorized By	Approx. Price

Equipment Rented Today	Rented From	Rate

Supervisor's Signature _____

DAY _____   DAILY LOG   20___ MAY 24

CONTRACTOR _____ JOB NAME _____ JOB NO _____

Work Performed Today _____

_____

_____

_____

_____

_____

_____

_____

_____

_____

_____

_____

_____

_____

_____

Problems - Delays _____

_____

_____

_____

Sub-Contractor Progress _____

_____

_____

_____

Special Assignments _____

_____

_____

| Weather | | | _____ |
| Temp. AM _____ PM _____ | | | |

| Safety Meeting _____ |

Work Force	No.
Superintendent	_____
Clerk	_____
Bricklayers	_____
Carpenters	_____
Cement Masons	_____
Electricians	_____
Iron Workers	_____
Laborers	_____
Operating Eng.	_____
Plumbers	_____
Pipe Fitters	_____
Sheet Metal	_____
Truck Drivers	_____
Total	_____

Equipment	Hrs.

Material Purchased

Extra Work	Authorized By	Approx. Price

Equipment Rented Today	Rented From	Rate

Supervisor's Signature _____

25 MAY 20____   DAILY LOG   DAY _____

CONTRACTOR _____ JOB NAME _____ JOB NO._____

Work Performed Today _____	Weather _____
_____	Temp. AM _____PM _____
_____	Safety Meeting _____

Work Force	No.
Superintendent	_____
Clerk	_____
Bricklayers	_____
Carpenters	_____
Cement Masons	_____
Electricians	_____
Iron Workers	_____
Laborers	_____
Operating Eng.	_____
Plumbers	_____
Pipe Fitters	_____
Sheet Metal	_____
Truck Drivers	_____
Total	_____

Problems - Delays _____

Sub-Contractor Progress _____

Equipment	Hrs.

Special Assignments _____

Material Purchased	

Extra Work	Authorized By	Approx. Price

Equipment Rented Today	Rented From	Rate

Supervisor's Signature _____

DAY _____   DAILY LOG   20____ MAY 26

CONTRACTOR _____ JOB NAME _____ JOB NO _____

Work Performed Today _____	Weather _____
_____	Temp. AM _____PM _____
_____	Safety Meeting _____

Work Force	No.
Superintendent	_____
Clerk	_____
Bricklayers	_____
Carpenters	_____
Cement Masons	_____
Electricians	_____
Iron Workers	_____
Laborers	_____
Operating Eng.	_____
Plumbers	_____
Pipe Fitters	_____
Sheet Metal	_____
Truck Drivers	_____
Total	_____

Problems - Delays _____

Sub-Contractor Progress _____

Equipment	Hrs.

Special Assignments _____

Extra Work	Authorized By	Approx. Price

Equipment Rented Today	Rented From	Rate

Material Purchased

Supervisor's Signature _____

27 MAY 20____   DAILY LOG   DAY _____

CONTRACTOR _____ JOB NAME _____ JOB NO._____

Work Performed Today _____	Weather _____
	Temp. AM _____ PM _____
	Safety Meeting _____
	Work Force **No.**
	Superintendent _____
	Clerk _____
	Bricklayers _____
	Carpenters _____
	Cement Masons _____
	Electricians _____
	Iron Workers _____
	Laborers _____
	Operating Eng. _____
	Plumbers _____
	Pipe Fitters _____
	Sheet Metal _____
	Truck Drivers _____
Problems - Delays _____	
	Total _____
Sub-Contractor Progress _____	Equipment / Hrs.

Equipment	Hrs.

Special Assignments _____

Material Purchased

Extra Work	Authorized By	Approx. Price

Equipment Rented Today	Rented From	Rate

Supervisor's Signature _____

DAY _____   DAILY LOG   20___ MAY 28

CONTRACTOR _____ JOB NAME _____ JOB NO _____

Work Performed Today _____	Weather _____
	Temp. AM _____ PM _____
	Safety Meeting _____

Work Force	No.
Superintendent	_____
Clerk	_____
Bricklayers	_____
Carpenters	_____
Cement Masons	_____
Electricians	_____
Iron Workers	_____
Laborers	_____
Operating Eng.	_____
Plumbers	_____
Pipe Fitters	_____
Sheet Metal	_____
Truck Drivers	_____
Total	_____

Problems - Delays _____

Equipment	Hrs.

Sub-Contractor Progress _____

Special Assignments _____

Extra Work	Authorized By	Approx. Price

Equipment Rented Today	Rented From	Rate

Material Purchased

Supervisor's Signature _____

29 MAY 20___   DAILY LOG   DAY _____

CONTRACTOR _____ JOB NAME _____ JOB NO._____

Work Performed Today _____

_____

_____

_____

_____

_____

_____

_____

_____

_____

_____

_____

_____

Problems - Delays _____

_____

_____

_____

Sub-Contractor Progress _____

_____

_____

_____

Special Assignments _____

_____

_____

Extra Work	Authorized By	Approx. Price

Equipment Rented Today	Rented From	Rate

Supervisor's Signature _____

Weather _____

Temp. AM _____PM _____

Safety Meeting _____

Work Force	No.
Superintendent	_____
Clerk	_____
Bricklayers	_____
Carpenters	_____
Cement Masons	_____
Electricians	_____
Iron Workers	_____
Laborers	_____
Operating Eng.	_____
Plumbers	_____
Pipe Fitters	_____
Sheet Metal	_____
Truck Drivers	_____
Total	_____

Equipment	Hrs.

Material Purchased

DAY _____   DAILY LOG   20___ MAY 30

CONTRACTOR _____ JOB NAME _____ JOB NO _____

Work Performed Today _____

_____

_____

_____

_____

_____

_____

_____

_____

_____

_____

_____

_____

Problems - Delays _____

_____

_____

_____

Sub-Contractor Progress _____

_____

_____

_____

Special Assignments _____

_____

_____

Weather	
Temp. AM _____ PM _____	
Safety Meeting _____	

Work Force	No.
Superintendent	_____
Clerk	_____
Bricklayers	_____
Carpenters	_____
Cement Masons	_____
Electricians	_____
Iron Workers	_____
Laborers	_____
Operating Eng.	_____
Plumbers	
Pipe Fitters	
Sheet Metal	_____
Truck Drivers	_____
Total	_____

Equipment	Hrs.

Extra Work	Authorized By	Approx. Price

Equipment Rented Today	Rented From	Rate

Material Purchased

Supervisor's Signature _____

31 MAY 20___   DAILY LOG   DAY _____

CONTRACTOR _____ JOB NAME _____ JOB NO._____

Work Performed Today _____

_____

_____

_____

_____

_____

_____

_____

_____

_____

_____

_____

_____

Problems - Delays _____

_____

_____

_____

Sub-Contractor Progress _____

_____

_____

Special Assignments _____

_____

_____

Weather	_____	

Temp. AM _____ PM _____

Safety Meeting _____

Work Force	No.
Superintendent	_____
Clerk	_____
Bricklayers	_____
Carpenters	_____
Cement Masons	_____
Electricians	_____
Iron Workers	_____
Laborers	_____
Operating Eng.	_____
Plumbers	_____
Pipe Fitters	_____
Sheet Metal	_____
Truck Drivers	_____
Total	_____

Equipment	Hrs.

Material Purchased	

Extra Work	Authorized By	Approx. Price

Equipment Rented Today	Rented From	Rate

Supervisor's Signature _____

DAY _____   DAILY LOG   20___ JUNE 1

CONTRACTOR _____ JOB NAME _____ JOB NO _____

Work Performed Today _____		Weather _____
		Temp. AM _____ PM _____
		Safety Meeting _____

Work Force	No.
Superintendent	_____
Clerk	_____
Bricklayers	_____
Carpenters	_____
Cement Masons	_____
Electricians	_____
Iron Workers	_____
Laborers	_____
Operating Eng.	_____
Plumbers	_____
Pipe Fitters	_____
Sheet Metal	
Truck Drivers	
Total	_____

Problems - Delays _____

Equipment	Hrs.

Sub-Contractor Progress _____

Special Assignments _____

Extra Work	Authorized By	Approx. Price

Equipment Rented Today	Rented From	Rate

Material Purchased

Supervisor's Signature _____

2 JUNE 20___   DAILY LOG   DAY _____

CONTRACTOR _____ JOB NAME _____ JOB NO._____

Work Performed Today _____	Weather _____
_____	Temp. AM _____PM _____
_____	Safety Meeting _____
_____	**Work Force** **No.**
_____	Superintendent _____
_____	Clerk _____
_____	Bricklayers _____
_____	Carpenters _____
_____	Cement Masons _____
_____	Electricians _____
_____	Iron Workers _____
_____	Laborers _____
_____	Operating Eng. _____
_____	Plumbers _____
_____	Pipe Fitters _____
_____	Sheet Metal _____
_____	Truck Drivers _____

Problems - Delays _____
_____
_____
_____

Total _____

Sub-Contractor Progress _____
_____
_____
_____

Equipment	Hrs.

Special Assignments _____
_____
_____

Extra Work	Authorized By	Approx. Price

Material Purchased

Equipment Rented Today	Rented From	Rate

Supervisor's Signature _____

DAY _____   DAILY LOG   20___ JUNE 3

CONTRACTOR _____ JOB NAME _____ JOB NO _____

Work Performed Today _____	Weather _____
_____	Temp. AM _____PM _____
_____	Safety Meeting _____

Work Force	No.
Superintendent	_____
Clerk	_____
Bricklayers	_____
Carpenters	_____
Cement Masons	_____
Electricians	_____
Iron Workers	_____
Laborers	_____
Operating Eng.	_____
Plumbers	_____
Pipe Fitters	_____
Sheet Metal	_____
Truck Drivers	_____
Total	_____

Problems - Delays _____

Equipment	Hrs.

Sub-Contractor Progress _____

Special Assignments _____

Extra Work	Authorized By	Approx. Price

Equipment Rented Today	Rented From	Rate

Material Purchased

Supervisor's Signature _____

4 JUNE 20___   DAILY LOG   DAY _____

CONTRACTOR _____ JOB NAME _____ JOB NO. _____

Work Performed Today _____

_____

_____

_____

_____

_____

_____

_____

_____

_____

_____

_____

_____

_____

Problems - Delays _____

_____

_____

_____

Sub-Contractor Progress _____

_____

_____

_____

Special Assignments _____

_____

_____

Weather	_____
Temp. AM _____ PM _____	
Safety Meeting _____	

Work Force	No.
Superintendent	_____
Clerk	_____
Bricklayers	_____
Carpenters	_____
Cement Masons	_____
Electricians	_____
Iron Workers	_____
Laborers	_____
Operating Eng.	_____
Plumbers	_____
Pipe Fitters	_____
Sheet Metal	_____
Truck Drivers	_____
Total	_____

Equipment	Hrs.

Extra Work	Authorized By	Approx. Price

Equipment Rented Today	Rented From	Rate

Material Purchased

Supervisor's Signature _____

DAY _____   DAILY LOG   20___ JUNE 5

CONTRACTOR _____ JOB NAME _____ JOB NO _____

Work Performed Today _____

_____

_____

_____

_____

_____

_____

_____

_____

_____

_____

_____

_____

_____

Problems - Delays _____

_____

_____

_____

Sub-Contractor Progress _____

_____

_____

Special Assignments _____

_____

_____

Extra Work	Authorized By	Approx. Price

Equipment Rented Today	Rented From	Rate

Supervisor's Signature _____

Weather _____

Temp. AM _____PM _____

Safety Meeting _____

Work Force	No.
Superintendent	_____
Clerk	_____
Bricklayers	_____
Carpenters	_____
Cement Masons	_____
Electricians	_____
Iron Workers	_____
Laborers	_____
Operating Eng.	_____
Plumbers	_____
Pipe Fitters	_____
Sheet Metal	_____
Truck Drivers	_____
Total	_____

Equipment	Hrs.

Material Purchased

6 JUNE 20___   DAILY LOG   DAY _____

CONTRACTOR _____ JOB NAME _____ JOB NO._____

Work Performed Today _____

_____

_____

_____

_____

_____

_____

_____

_____

_____

_____

_____

_____

Problems - Delays _____

_____

_____

_____

Sub-Contractor Progress _____

_____

_____

_____

Special Assignments _____

_____

_____

Extra Work	Authorized By	Approx. Price

Equipment Rented Today	Rented From	Rate

Supervisor's Signature _____

Weather _____

Temp. AM _____ PM _____

Safety Meeting _____

Work Force	No.
Superintendent	
Clerk	
Bricklayers	
Carpenters	
Cement Masons	
Electricians	
Iron Workers	
Laborers	
Operating Eng.	
Plumbers	
Pipe Fitters	
Sheet Metal	
Truck Drivers	
Total	

Equipment	Hrs.

Material Purchased

DAY _____   DAILY LOG   20___ JUNE 7

CONTRACTOR _____ JOB NAME _____ JOB NO _____

| Work Performed Today | Weather _____ |
| | Temp. AM _____PM _____ |

| | Safety Meeting _____ |

Work Force	No.
Superintendent	_____
Clerk	_____
Bricklayers	_____
Carpenters	_____
Cement Masons	_____
Electricians	_____
Iron Workers	_____
Laborers	_____
Operating Eng.	_____
Plumbers	
Pipe Fitters	
Sheet Metal	_____
Truck Drivers	_____
Total	_____

Problems - Delays _____

Equipment	Hrs.

Sub-Contractor Progress _____

Special Assignments _____

Material Purchased	

Extra Work	Authorized By	Approx. Price

Equipment Rented Today	Rented From	Rate

Supervisor's Signature _____

8 JUNE 20___   DAILY LOG   DAY _____

CONTRACTOR _____ JOB NAME _____ JOB NO._____

Work Performed Today _____

| Weather _____ |
| Temp. AM _____ PM _____ |

Safety Meeting _____

Work Force	No.
Superintendent	_____
Clerk	_____
Bricklayers	_____
Carpenters	_____
Cement Masons	_____
Electricians	_____
Iron Workers	_____
Laborers	_____
Operating Eng.	_____
Plumbers	_____
Pipe Fitters	_____
Sheet Metal	_____
Truck Drivers	_____
Total	_____

Problems - Delays _____

Sub-Contractor Progress _____

Equipment	Hrs.

Special Assignments _____

Extra Work	Authorized By	Approx. Price

Equipment Rented Today	Rented From	Rate

Material Purchased

Supervisor's Signature _____

DAY _____   DAILY LOG   20____ JUNE 9

CONTRACTOR _____ JOB NAME _____ JOB NO _____

Work Performed Today _____	Weather _____
_____	Temp. AM _____ PM _____
_____	Safety Meeting _____

Work Force	No.
Superintendent	_____
Clerk	_____
Bricklayers	_____
Carpenters	_____
Cement Masons	_____
Electricians	_____
Iron Workers	_____
Laborers	_____
Operating Eng.	_____
Plumbers	_____
Pipe Fitters	_____
Sheet Metal	_____
Truck Drivers	_____
Total	_____

Problems - Delays _____

Equipment	Hrs.

Sub-Contractor Progress _____

Special Assignments _____

Extra Work	Authorized By	Approx. Price

Equipment Rented Today	Rented From	Rate

Material Purchased

Supervisor's Signature _____

10 JUNE 20___   DAILY LOG   DAY _____

CONTRACTOR _____ JOB NAME _____ JOB NO._____

Work Performed Today _____	Weather _____
	Temp. AM _____PM _____
	Safety Meeting _____

Work Force	No.
Superintendent	_____
Clerk	_____
Bricklayers	_____
Carpenters	_____
Cement Masons	_____
Electricians	_____
Iron Workers	_____
Laborers	_____
Operating Eng.	_____
Plumbers	_____
Pipe Fitters	_____
Sheet Metal	_____
Truck Drivers	_____
Total	_____

Problems - Delays _____

Sub-Contractor Progress _____

Equipment	Hrs.

Special Assignments _____

Extra Work	Authorized By	Approx. Price

Equipment Rented Today	Rented From	Rate

Material Purchased

Supervisor's Signature _____

DAY _____   DAILY LOG   20___ JUNE 11

CONTRACTOR _____ JOB NAME _____ JOB NO _____

Work Performed Today _____

_____

_____

_____

_____

_____

_____

_____

_____

_____

_____

_____

_____

Problems - Delays _____

_____

_____

_____

Sub-Contractor Progress _____

_____

_____

_____

Special Assignments _____

_____

_____

Weather	
Temp. AM _____ PM _____	
Safety Meeting _____	

Work Force	No.
Superintendent	_____
Clerk	_____
Bricklayers	_____
Carpenters	_____
Cement Masons	_____
Electricians	_____
Iron Workers	_____
Laborers	_____
Operating Eng.	_____
Plumbers	_____
Pipe Fitters	_____
Sheet Metal	_____
Truck Drivers	_____
Total	_____

Equipment	Hrs.

Extra Work	Authorized By	Approx. Price

Equipment Rented Today	Rented From	Rate

Material Purchased

Supervisor's Signature _____

12 JUNE 20___   DAILY LOG   DAY _____

CONTRACTOR _____ JOB NAME _____ JOB NO. _____

Work Performed Today _____

_____

_____

_____

_____

_____

_____

_____

_____

_____

_____

_____

_____

_____

Problems - Delays _____

_____

_____

_____

Sub-Contractor Progress _____

_____

_____

_____

Special Assignments _____

_____

_____

Extra Work	Authorized By	Approx. Price

Equipment Rented Today	Rented From	Rate

Supervisor's Signature _____

Weather _____

Temp. AM _____ PM _____

Safety Meeting _____

Work Force	No.
Superintendent	
Clerk	
Bricklayers	
Carpenters	
Cement Masons	
Electricians	
Iron Workers	
Laborers	
Operating Eng.	
Plumbers	
Pipe Fitters	
Sheet Metal	
Truck Drivers	
Total	

Equipment	Hrs.

Material Purchased

DAY _____   DAILY LOG   20___ JUNE 13

CONTRACTOR _____ JOB NAME _____ JOB NO _____

Work Performed Today _____

_____

_____

_____

_____

_____

_____

_____

_____

_____

_____

_____

_____

_____

Problems - Delays _____

_____

_____

_____

Sub-Contractor Progress _____

_____

_____

_____

Special Assignments _____

_____

_____

Extra Work	Authorized By	Approx. Price

Equipment Rented Today	Rented From	Rate

Supervisor's Signature _____

| Weather _____ |
| Temp. AM _____ PM _____ |
| Safety Meeting _____ |

Work Force	No.
Superintendent	_____
Clerk	_____
Bricklayers	_____
Carpenters	_____
Cement Masons	_____
Electricians	_____
Iron Workers	_____
Laborers	_____
Operating Eng.	_____
Plumbers	_____
Pipe Fitters	_____
Sheet Metal	_____
Truck Drivers	_____
Total	_____

Equipment	Hrs.

Material Purchased

14 JUNE 20___   DAILY LOG   DAY _____

CONTRACTOR _____ JOB NAME _____ JOB NO._____

Work Performed Today _____

_____

_____

_____

_____

_____

_____

_____

_____

_____

_____

_____

_____

Problems - Delays _____

_____

_____

_____

Sub-Contractor Progress _____

_____

_____

_____

Special Assignments _____

_____

_____

| Weather _____ |
| Temp. AM _____PM _____ |
| Safety Meeting _____ |

Work Force	No.
Superintendent	_____
Clerk	_____
Bricklayers	_____
Carpenters	_____
Cement Masons	_____
Electricians	_____
Iron Workers	_____
Laborers	_____
Operating Eng.	_____
Plumbers	_____
Pipe Fitters	_____
Sheet Metal	_____
Truck Drivers	_____
Total	_____

Equipment	Hrs.

Material Purchased

Extra Work	Authorized By	Approx. Price

Equipment Rented Today	Rented From	Rate

Supervisor's Signature _____

DAY _____   DAILY LOG   20___ JUNE 15

CONTRACTOR _____ JOB NAME _____ JOB NO _____

Work Performed Today _____	Weather _____
_____	Temp. AM _____PM _____
_____	Safety Meeting _____

Work Force	No.
Superintendent	_____
Clerk	_____
Bricklayers	_____
Carpenters	_____
Cement Masons	_____
Electricians	_____
Iron Workers	_____
Laborers	_____
Operating Eng.	_____
Plumbers	_____
Pipe Fitters	_____
Sheet Metal	_____
Truck Drivers	_____
Total	_____

Problems - Delays _____

Equipment	Hrs.

Sub-Contractor Progress _____

Special Assignments _____

Material Purchased

Extra Work	Authorized By	Approx. Price

Equipment Rented Today	Rented From	Rate

Supervisor's Signature _____

16 JUNE 20___   DAILY LOG   DAY _____

CONTRACTOR _____ JOB NAME _____ JOB NO._____

Work Performed Today _____

_____

_____

_____

_____

_____

_____

_____

_____

_____

_____

_____

_____

Problems - Delays _____

_____

_____

_____

Sub-Contractor Progress _____

_____

_____

_____

Special Assignments _____

_____

_____

Weather	
Temp. AM _____ PM _____	
Safety Meeting _____	

Work Force	No.
Superintendent	_____
Clerk	_____
Bricklayers	_____
Carpenters	_____
Cement Masons	_____
Electricians	_____
Iron Workers	_____
Laborers	_____
Operating Eng.	_____
Plumbers	_____
Pipe Fitters	_____
Sheet Metal	_____
Truck Drivers	_____
Total	_____

Equipment	Hrs.

Extra Work	Authorized By	Approx. Price

Equipment Rented Today	Rented From	Rate

Material Purchased

Supervisor's Signature _____

DAY _____   DAILY LOG   20___ JUNE 17

CONTRACTOR _____ JOB NAME _____ JOB NO _____

Work Performed Today _____

_____

_____

_____

_____

_____

_____

_____

_____

_____

_____

_____

_____

_____

Problems - Delays _____

_____

_____

_____

Sub-Contractor Progress _____

_____

_____

_____

Special Assignments _____

_____

_____

| Weather _____ |
| Temp. AM _____PM _____ |
| Safety Meeting _____ |

Work Force	No.
Superintendent	_____
Clerk	_____
Bricklayers	_____
Carpenters	_____
Cement Masons	_____
Electricians	_____
Iron Workers	_____
Laborers	_____
Operating Eng.	_____
Plumbers	_____
Pipe Fitters	_____
Sheet Metal	_____
Truck Drivers	_____
Total	_____

Equipment	Hrs.

Material Purchased

Extra Work	Authorized By	Approx. Price

Equipment Rented Today	Rented From	Rate

Supervisor's Signature _____

18 JUNE 20___   DAILY LOG   DAY _____

CONTRACTOR _____ JOB NAME _____ JOB NO._____

Work Performed Today _____	Weather _____
	Temp. AM _____PM _____

Safety Meeting _____

Work Force	No.
Superintendent	_____
Clerk	_____
Bricklayers	_____
Carpenters	_____
Cement Masons	_____
Electricians	_____
Iron Workers	_____
Laborers	_____
Operating Eng.	_____
Plumbers	_____
Pipe Fitters	_____
Sheet Metal	_____
Truck Drivers	_____
Total	_____

Problems - Delays _____

Equipment	Hrs.

Sub-Contractor Progress _____

Special Assignments _____

Extra Work	Authorized By	Approx. Price

Material Purchased	

Equipment Rented Today	Rented From	Rate

Supervisor's Signature _____

DAY _____   DAILY LOG   20___ JUNE 19

CONTRACTOR _____ JOB NAME _____ JOB NO _____

Work Performed Today _____	Weather _____
_____	Temp. AM _____ PM _____
_____	Safety Meeting _____

Work Force	No.
Superintendent	_____
Clerk	_____
Bricklayers	_____
Carpenters	_____
Cement Masons	_____
Electricians	_____
Iron Workers	_____
Laborers	_____
Operating Eng.	_____
Plumbers	_____
Pipe Fitters	_____
Sheet Metal	_____
Truck Drivers	_____
Total	_____

Problems - Delays _____

Sub-Contractor Progress _____

Equipment	Hrs.

Special Assignments _____

Extra Work	Authorized By	Approx. Price	Material Purchased

Equipment Rented Today	Rented From	Rate	

Supervisor's Signature _____

20 JUNE 20___   DAILY LOG   DAY _____

CONTRACTOR _____ JOB NAME _____ JOB NO._____

Work Performed Today _____	Weather _____
_____	Temp. AM _____PM _____
_____	
_____	Safety Meeting _____
_____	

Work Force	No.
Superintendent	_____
Clerk	_____
Bricklayers	_____
Carpenters	_____
Cement Masons	_____
Electricians	_____
Iron Workers	_____
Laborers	_____
Operating Eng.	_____
Plumbers	_____
Pipe Fitters	_____
Sheet Metal	_____
Truck Drivers	_____
Total	_____

Problems - Delays _____

Sub-Contractor Progress _____

Equipment	Hrs.

Special Assignments _____

Extra Work	Authorized By	Approx. Price

Equipment Rented Today	Rented From	Rate

Material Purchased

Supervisor's Signature _____

DAY _____   DAILY LOG   20___ JUNE 21

CONTRACTOR _____ JOB NAME _____ JOB NO _____

Work Performed Today _____

_____

_____

_____

_____

_____

_____

_____

_____

_____

_____

_____

_____

_____

Problems - Delays _____

_____

_____

_____

Sub-Contractor Progress _____

_____

_____

_____

Special Assignments _____

_____

_____

Weather	
Temp. AM _____ PM _____	
Safety Meeting _____	

Work Force	No.
Superintendent	_____
Clerk	_____
Bricklayers	_____
Carpenters	_____
Cement Masons	_____
Electricians	_____
Iron Workers	_____
Laborers	_____
Operating Eng.	_____
Plumbers	_____
Pipe Fitters	_____
Sheet Metal	_____
Truck Drivers	_____
Total	_____

Equipment	Hrs.

Material Purchased	

Extra Work	Authorized By	Approx. Price

Equipment Rented Today	Rented From	Rate

Supervisor's Signature _____

22 JUNE 20___   DAILY LOG   DAY _____

CONTRACTOR _____ JOB NAME _____ JOB NO._____

Work Performed Today _____	Weather _____
	Temp. AM _____PM _____

Work Performed Today _____
_____
_____
_____
_____
_____
_____
_____
_____
_____
_____
_____
_____

Weather _____

Temp. AM _____PM _____

Safety Meeting _____

Work Force	No.
Superintendent	_____
Clerk	_____
Bricklayers	_____
Carpenters	_____
Cement Masons	_____
Electricians	_____
Iron Workers	_____
Laborers	_____
Operating Eng.	_____
Plumbers	_____
Pipe Fitters	_____
Sheet Metal	_____
Truck Drivers	_____
Total	_____

Problems - Delays _____
_____
_____
_____
_____

Sub-Contractor Progress _____
_____
_____
_____

Special Assignments _____
_____
_____

Equipment	Hrs.

Extra Work	Authorized By	Approx. Price

Equipment Rented Today	Rented From	Rate

Material Purchased

Material Purchased

Supervisor's Signature _____

DAY _____   DAILY LOG   20___ JUNE 23

CONTRACTOR _____ JOB NAME _____ JOB NO _____

Work Performed Today _____

_____

_____

_____

_____

_____

_____

_____

_____

_____

_____

_____

Problems - Delays _____

_____

_____

_____

Sub-Contractor Progress _____

_____

_____

_____

Special Assignments _____

_____

_____

| Weather _____ |
| Temp. AM _____ PM _____ |
| Safety Meeting _____ |

Work Force	No.
Superintendent	_____
Clerk	_____
Bricklayers	_____
Carpenters	_____
Cement Masons	_____
Electricians	_____
Iron Workers	_____
Laborers	_____
Operating Eng.	_____
Plumbers	_____
Pipe Fitters	_____
Sheet Metal	_____
Truck Drivers	_____
Total	_____

Equipment	Hrs.

Extra Work	Authorized By	Approx. Price

Equipment Rented Today	Rented From	Rate

Material Purchased

Supervisor's Signature _____

24 JUNE 20___   DAILY LOG   DAY _____

CONTRACTOR _____ JOB NAME _____ JOB NO._____

Work Performed Today _____

_____

_____

_____

_____

_____

_____

_____

_____

_____

_____

_____

_____

_____

_____

Problems - Delays _____

_____

_____

_____

Sub-Contractor Progress _____

_____

_____

_____

Special Assignments _____

_____

_____

Weather	_____
Temp. AM _____ PM _____	
Safety Meeting _____	

Work Force	No.
Superintendent	_____
Clerk	_____
Bricklayers	_____
Carpenters	_____
Cement Masons	_____
Electricians	_____
Iron Workers	_____
Laborers	_____
Operating Eng.	_____
Plumbers	_____
Pipe Fitters	_____
Sheet Metal	_____
Truck Drivers	_____
Total	_____

Equipment	Hrs.

Extra Work	Authorized By	Approx. Price

Equipment Rented Today	Rented From	Rate

Material Purchased

Supervisor's Signature _____

DAY _____   DAILY LOG   20___ JUNE 25

CONTRACTOR _____ JOB NAME _____ JOB NO _____

Work Performed Today _____

_____

_____

_____

_____

_____

_____

_____

_____

_____

_____

_____

_____

_____

Problems - Delays _____

_____

_____

_____

Sub-Contractor Progress _____

_____

_____

_____

Special Assignments _____

_____

_____

Weather	_____	
Temp. AM _____ PM _____		
Safety Meeting _____		

Work Force	No.
Superintendent	_____
Clerk	_____
Bricklayers	_____
Carpenters	_____
Cement Masons	_____
Electricians	_____
Iron Workers	_____
Laborers	_____
Operating Eng.	_____
Plumbers	_____
Pipe Fitters	_____
Sheet Metal	_____
Truck Drivers	_____
Total	_____

Equipment	Hrs.

Extra Work	Authorized By	Approx. Price

Equipment Rented Today	Rented From	Rate

Material Purchased

Supervisor's Signature _____

26 JUNE 20____   DAILY LOG   DAY _____

CONTRACTOR _____ JOB NAME _____ JOB NO._____

Work Performed Today _____

_____
_____
_____
_____
_____
_____
_____
_____
_____
_____
_____
_____
_____

Problems - Delays _____
_____
_____
_____

Sub-Contractor Progress _____
_____
_____
_____

Special Assignments _____
_____
_____

Extra Work	Authorized By	Approx. Price

Equipment Rented Today	Rented From	Rate

Supervisor's Signature _____

| Weather _____ |
| Temp. AM _____ PM _____ |

Safety Meeting _____

Work Force	No.
Superintendent	_____
Clerk	_____
Bricklayers	_____
Carpenters	_____
Cement Masons	_____
Electricians	_____
Iron Workers	_____
Laborers	_____
Operating Eng.	_____
Plumbers	_____
Pipe Fitters	_____
Sheet Metal	_____
Truck Drivers	_____
Total	_____

Equipment	Hrs.

Material Purchased

DAY _____   DAILY LOG   20___ JUNE 27

CONTRACTOR _____ JOB NAME _____ JOB NO _____

Work Performed Today _____

_____

_____

_____

_____

_____

_____

_____

_____

_____

_____

_____

_____

Problems - Delays _____

_____

_____

_____

Sub-Contractor Progress _____

_____

_____

_____

Special Assignments _____

_____

_____

| Weather _____ |
| Temp. AM _____ PM _____ |
| Safety Meeting _____ |

Work Force	No.
Superintendent	_____
Clerk	_____
Bricklayers	_____
Carpenters	_____
Cement Masons	_____
Electricians	_____
Iron Workers	_____
Laborers	_____
Operating Eng.	_____
Plumbers	_____
Pipe Fitters	_____
Sheet Metal	_____
Truck Drivers	_____
Total	_____

Equipment	Hrs.

Extra Work	Authorized By	Approx. Price

Equipment Rented Today	Rented From	Rate

Material Purchased

Supervisor's Signature _____

28 JUNE 20___   DAILY LOG   DAY _____

CONTRACTOR _____ JOB NAME _____ JOB NO._____

Work Performed Today _____	Weather _____
	Temp. AM _____ PM _____
	Safety Meeting _____

Work Force	No.
Superintendent	_____
Clerk	_____
Bricklayers	_____
Carpenters	_____
Cement Masons	_____
Electricians	_____
Iron Workers	_____
Laborers	_____
Operating Eng.	_____
Plumbers	_____
Pipe Fitters	_____
Sheet Metal	_____
Truck Drivers	_____
Total	_____

Problems - Delays _____

Sub-Contractor Progress _____

Equipment	Hrs.

Special Assignments _____

Extra Work	Authorized By	Approx. Price

Equipment Rented Today	Rented From	Rate

Material Purchased

Supervisor's Signature _____

DAY _____ DAILY LOG 20___ JUNE 29

CONTRACTOR _____ JOB NAME _____ JOB NO _____

Work Performed Today _____

_____

_____

_____

_____

_____

_____

_____

_____

_____

_____

_____

_____

_____

Problems - Delays _____

_____

_____

_____

Sub-Contractor Progress _____

_____

_____

_____

Special Assignments _____

_____

_____

Weather		
Temp. AM _____ PM _____		
Safety Meeting _____		

Work Force	No.
Superintendent	_____
Clerk	_____
Bricklayers	_____
Carpenters	_____
Cement Masons	_____
Electricians	_____
Iron Workers	_____
Laborers	_____
Operating Eng.	_____
Plumbers	_____
Pipe Fitters	_____
Sheet Metal	_____
Truck Drivers	_____
Total	_____

Equipment	Hrs.

Extra Work	Authorized By	Approx. Price

Equipment Rented Today	Rented From	Rate

Material Purchased

Supervisor's Signature _____

30 JUNE 20___   DAILY LOG   DAY _____

CONTRACTOR _____ JOB NAME _____ JOB NO._____

Work Performed Today _____

_____

_____

_____

_____

_____

_____

_____

_____

_____

_____

_____

_____

Problems - Delays _____

_____

_____

_____

Sub-Contractor Progress _____

_____

_____

Special Assignments _____

_____

_____

| Weather _____ |
| Temp. AM _____PM _____ |
| Safety Meeting _____ |

Work Force	No.
Superintendent	_____
Clerk	_____
Bricklayers	_____
Carpenters	_____
Cement Masons	_____
Electricians	_____
Iron Workers	_____
Laborers	_____
Operating Eng.	_____
Plumbers	_____
Pipe Fitters	_____
Sheet Metal	_____
Truck Drivers	_____
Total	_____

Equipment	Hrs.

Extra Work	Authorized By	Approx. Price

Equipment Rented Today	Rented From	Rate

Material Purchased

Supervisor's Signature _____

DAY _____   DAILY LOG   20___ JULY 1

CONTRACTOR _____ JOB NAME _____ JOB NO _____

Work Performed Today _____	Weather _____
	Temp. AM _____ PM _____

Safety Meeting _____

Work Force	No.
Superintendent	_____
Clerk	_____
Bricklayers	_____
Carpenters	_____
Cement Masons	_____
Electricians	_____
Iron Workers	_____
Laborers	_____
Operating Eng.	_____
Plumbers	_____
Pipe Fitters	_____
Sheet Metal	_____
Truck Drivers	_____
Total	_____

Problems - Delays _____

Equipment	Hrs.

Sub-Contractor Progress _____

Special Assignments _____

Extra Work	Authorized By	Approx. Price

Equipment Rented Today	Rented From	Rate

Material Purchased

Supervisor's Signature _____

2 JULY 20___   DAILY LOG   DAY _____

CONTRACTOR _____ JOB NAME _____ JOB NO._____

Work Performed Today _____	Weather _____
	Temp. AM _____PM _____
	Safety Meeting _____

Work Force	No.
Superintendent	_____
Clerk	_____
Bricklayers	_____
Carpenters	_____
Cement Masons	_____
Electricians	_____
Iron Workers	_____
Laborers	_____
Operating Eng.	_____
Plumbers	_____
Pipe Fitters	_____
Sheet Metal	_____
Truck Drivers	_____
Total	_____

Problems - Delays _____

Equipment	Hrs.

Sub-Contractor Progress _____

Special Assignments _____

Extra Work	Authorized By	Approx. Price

Equipment Rented Today	Rented From	Rate

Material Purchased

Supervisor's Signature _____

DAY _____   DAILY LOG   20___ JULY 3

CONTRACTOR _____ JOB NAME _____ JOB NO _____

Work Performed Today _____	Weather _____
	Temp. AM _____PM _____
	Safety Meeting _____

Work Force	No.
Superintendent	_____
Clerk	_____
Bricklayers	_____
Carpenters	_____
Cement Masons	_____
Electricians	_____
Iron Workers	_____
Laborers	_____
Operating Eng.	_____
Plumbers	_____
Pipe Fitters	_____
Sheet Metal	_____
Truck Drivers	_____
Total	_____

Problems - Delays _____

Equipment	Hrs.

Sub-Contractor Progress _____

Special Assignments _____

Extra Work	Authorized By	Approx. Price

Equipment Rented Today	Rented From	Rate

Material Purchased

Supervisor's Signature _____

4 JULY 20____   DAILY LOG   DAY _____

CONTRACTOR _____ JOB NAME _____ JOB NO._____

Work Performed Today _____	Weather _____
_____	Temp. AM _____PM _____
_____	Safety Meeting _____

Work Force	**No.**
Superintendent	_____
Clerk	_____
Bricklayers	_____
Carpenters	_____
Cement Masons	_____
Electricians	_____
Iron Workers	_____
Laborers	_____
Operating Eng.	_____
Plumbers	_____
Pipe Fitters	_____
Sheet Metal	_____
Truck Drivers	_____
Total	_____

Problems - Delays _____

Sub-Contractor Progress _____

Equipment	Hrs.

Special Assignments _____

Extra Work	Authorized By	Approx. Price

Equipment Rented Today	Rented From	Rate

Material Purchased

Supervisor's Signature _____

DAY _____   DAILY LOG   20___ JULY 5

CONTRACTOR _____ JOB NAME _____ JOB NO _____

Work Performed Today _____	Weather _____
_____	Temp. AM _____PM _____
_____	Safety Meeting _____

Work Force	No.
Superintendent	_____
Clerk	_____
Bricklayers	_____
Carpenters	_____
Cement Masons	_____
Electricians	_____
Iron Workers	_____
Laborers	_____
Operating Eng.	_____
Plumbers	_____
Pipe Fitters	_____
Sheet Metal	_____
Truck Drivers	_____
Total	_____

Problems - Delays _____

Sub-Contractor Progress _____

Equipment	Hrs.

Special Assignments _____

Extra Work	Authorized By	Approx. Price

Equipment Rented Today	Rented From	Rate

Material Purchased

Supervisor's Signature _____

6 JULY 20____   DAILY LOG   DAY _____

CONTRACTOR _____ JOB NAME _____ JOB NO._____

Work Performed Today _____	Weather _____
_____	Temp. AM _____ PM _____
_____	Safety Meeting _____

Work Force	No.
Superintendent	_____
Clerk	_____
Bricklayers	_____
Carpenters	_____
Cement Masons	_____
Electricians	_____
Iron Workers	_____
Laborers	_____
Operating Eng.	_____
Plumbers	_____
Pipe Fitters	_____
Sheet Metal	_____
Truck Drivers	_____
Total	_____

Problems - Delays _____

Sub-Contractor Progress _____

Equipment	Hrs.

Special Assignments _____

Material Purchased	

Extra Work	Authorized By	Approx. Price

Equipment Rented Today	Rented From	Rate

Supervisor's Signature _____

DAY _____   DAILY LOG   20___ JULY 7

CONTRACTOR _____ JOB NAME _____ JOB NO _____

Work Performed Today _____	Weather _____
	Temp. AM _____ PM _____
	Safety Meeting _____

Work Force	No.
Superintendent	_____
Clerk	_____
Bricklayers	_____
Carpenters	_____
Cement Masons	_____
Electricians	_____
Iron Workers	_____
Laborers	_____
Operating Eng.	_____
Plumbers	_____
Pipe Fitters	_____
Sheet Metal	_____
Truck Drivers	_____
Total	_____

Problems - Delays _____

Equipment	Hrs.

Sub-Contractor Progress _____

Special Assignments _____

Material Purchased	

Extra Work	Authorized By	Approx. Price

Equipment Rented Today	Rented From	Rate

Supervisor's Signature _____

8 JULY 20___ DAILY LOG DAY _____

CONTRACTOR _____ JOB NAME _____ JOB NO. _____

Work Performed Today _____	Weather _____
	Temp. AM _____ PM _____
	Safety Meeting _____

Work Force	**No.**
Superintendent	_____
Clerk	_____
Bricklayers	_____
Carpenters	_____
Cement Masons	_____
Electricians	_____
Iron Workers	_____
Laborers	_____
Operating Eng.	_____
Plumbers	_____
Pipe Fitters	_____
Sheet Metal	_____
Truck Drivers	_____
Total	_____

Problems - Delays _____

Sub-Contractor Progress _____

Equipment	Hrs.

Special Assignments _____

Material Purchased	

Extra Work	Authorized By	Approx. Price

Equipment Rented Today	Rented From	Rate

Supervisor's Signature _____

DAY _____   DAILY LOG   20___ JULY 9

CONTRACTOR _____ JOB NAME _____ JOB NO _____

Work Performed Today _____

_____

_____

_____

_____

_____

_____

_____

_____

_____

_____

_____

_____

_____

Problems - Delays _____

_____

_____

_____

Sub-Contractor Progress _____

_____

_____

_____

Special Assignments _____

_____

_____

Extra Work	Authorized By	Approx. Price

Equipment Rented Today	Rented From	Rate

Supervisor's Signature _____

Weather _____

Temp. AM _____PM _____

Safety Meeting _____

Work Force	No.
Superintendent	_____
Clerk	_____
Bricklayers	_____
Carpenters	_____
Cement Masons	_____
Electricians	_____
Iron Workers	_____
Laborers	_____
Operating Eng.	_____
Plumbers	_____
Pipe Fitters	_____
Sheet Metal	_____
Truck Drivers	_____
Total	_____

Equipment	Hrs.

Material Purchased

10 JULY 20____   DAILY LOG   DAY _____

CONTRACTOR _____ JOB NAME _____ JOB NO._____

Work Performed Today _____	Weather _____
_____	Temp. AM _____PM _____
_____	Safety Meeting _____

Work Force	No.
Superintendent	_____
Clerk	_____
Bricklayers	_____
Carpenters	_____
Cement Masons	_____
Electricians	_____
Iron Workers	_____
Laborers	_____
Operating Eng.	_____
Plumbers	_____
Pipe Fitters	_____
Sheet Metal	_____
Truck Drivers	_____
Total	_____

Problems - Delays _____

Sub-Contractor Progress _____

Equipment	Hrs.

Special Assignments _____

Extra Work	Authorized By	Approx. Price

Equipment Rented Today	Rented From	Rate

Material Purchased

Supervisor's Signature _____

DAY _____   DAILY LOG   20___ JULY 11

CONTRACTOR _____ JOB NAME _____ JOB NO _____

Work Performed Today _____	Weather _____
	Temp. AM _____ PM _____
	Safety Meeting _____

Work Force	No.
Superintendent	_____
Clerk	_____
Bricklayers	_____
Carpenters	_____
Cement Masons	_____
Electricians	_____
Iron Workers	_____
Laborers	_____
Operating Eng.	_____
Plumbers	_____
Pipe Fitters	_____
Sheet Metal	_____
Truck Drivers	_____
Total	_____

Problems - Delays _____

Equipment	Hrs.

Sub-Contractor Progress _____

Special Assignments _____

Material Purchased		

Extra Work	Authorized By	Approx. Price

Equipment Rented Today	Rented From	Rate

Supervisor's Signature _____

12 JULY 20___   DAILY LOG   DAY _____

CONTRACTOR _____ JOB NAME _____ JOB NO._____

Work Performed Today _____	Weather _____
_____	Temp. AM _____PM _____
_____	Safety Meeting _____
_____	**Work Force** **No.**

Work Performed Today _____

Weather _____

Temp. AM _____ PM _____

Safety Meeting _____

Work Force	**No.**
Superintendent	_____
Clerk	_____
Bricklayers	_____
Carpenters	_____
Cement Masons	_____
Electricians	_____
Iron Workers	_____
Laborers	_____
Operating Eng.	_____
Plumbers	_____
Pipe Fitters	_____
Sheet Metal	_____
Truck Drivers	_____
Total	_____

Problems - Delays _____

Sub-Contractor Progress _____

Equipment	Hrs.

Special Assignments _____

Extra Work	Authorized By	Approx. Price

Equipment Rented Today	Rented From	Rate

Material Purchased

Supervisor's Signature _____

DAY _____   DAILY LOG   20___ JULY 13

CONTRACTOR _____ JOB NAME _____ JOB NO _____

Work Performed Today _____

_____

_____

_____

_____

_____

_____

_____

_____

_____

_____

_____

_____

Problems - Delays _____

_____

_____

_____

Sub-Contractor Progress _____

_____

_____

_____

Special Assignments _____

_____

_____

Weather		
Temp. AM _____ PM _____		
Safety Meeting _____		

Work Force	No.
Superintendent	_____
Clerk	_____
Bricklayers	_____
Carpenters	_____
Cement Masons	_____
Electricians	_____
Iron Workers	_____
Laborers	_____
Operating Eng.	_____
Plumbers	
Pipe Fitters	
Sheet Metal	_____
Truck Drivers	_____
Total	_____

Equipment	Hrs.

Material Purchased

Extra Work	Authorized By	Approx. Price

Equipment Rented Today	Rented From	Rate

Supervisor's Signature _____

14 JULY 20___   DAILY LOG   DAY _____

CONTRACTOR _____ JOB NAME _____ JOB NO._____

Work Performed Today _____

_____

_____

_____

_____

_____

_____

_____

_____

_____

_____

_____

_____

_____

Problems - Delays _____

_____

_____

_____

Sub-Contractor Progress _____

_____

_____

_____

Special Assignments _____

_____

_____

| Weather _____ |
| Temp. AM _____ PM _____ |

| Safety Meeting _____ |

Work Force	No.
Superintendent	_____
Clerk	_____
Bricklayers	_____
Carpenters	_____
Cement Masons	_____
Electricians	_____
Iron Workers	_____
Laborers	_____
Operating Eng.	_____
Plumbers	_____
Pipe Fitters	_____
Sheet Metal	_____
Truck Drivers	_____
Total	_____

Equipment	Hrs.

Extra Work	Authorized By	Approx. Price

Equipment Rented Today	Rented From	Rate

Material Purchased

Supervisor's Signature _____

DAY _____   DAILY LOG   20___ JULY 15

CONTRACTOR _____ JOB NAME _____ JOB NO _____

Work Performed Today _____	Weather _____

Work Performed Today _____

_____

_____

_____

_____

_____

_____

_____

_____

_____

_____

_____

_____

_____

Problems - Delays _____

_____

_____

_____

_____

Sub-Contractor Progress _____

_____

_____

_____

Special Assignments _____

_____

_____

Weather _____

Temp. AM _____ PM _____

Safety Meeting _____

Work Force	No.
Superintendent	_____
Clerk	_____
Bricklayers	_____
Carpenters	_____
Cement Masons	_____
Electricians	_____
Iron Workers	_____
Laborers	_____
Operating Eng.	_____
Plumbers	_____
Pipe Fitters	_____
Sheet Metal	_____
Truck Drivers	_____
Total	_____

Equipment	Hrs.

Extra Work	Authorized By	Approx. Price

Equipment Rented Today	Rented From	Rate

Material Purchased

Supervisor's Signature _____

16 JULY 20___   DAILY LOG   DAY _____

CONTRACTOR _____ JOB NAME _____ JOB NO._____

Work Performed Today _____

_____

_____

_____

_____

_____

_____

_____

_____

_____

_____

_____

_____

Problems - Delays _____

_____

_____

_____

Sub-Contractor Progress _____

_____

_____

_____

Special Assignments _____

_____

_____

Weather	_____
Temp. AM _____ PM _____	
Safety Meeting _____	

Work Force	No.
Superintendent	_____
Clerk	_____
Bricklayers	_____
Carpenters	_____
Cement Masons	_____
Electricians	_____
Iron Workers	_____
Laborers	_____
Operating Eng.	_____
Plumbers	_____
Pipe Fitters	_____
Sheet Metal	_____
Truck Drivers	_____
Total	_____

Equipment	Hrs.

Extra Work	Authorized By	Approx. Price

Equipment Rented Today	Rented From	Rate

Material Purchased

Supervisor's Signature _____

DAY _____   DAILY LOG   20___ JULY 17

CONTRACTOR _____ JOB NAME _____ JOB NO _____

Work Performed Today _____	Weather _____
_____	Temp. AM _____ PM _____
_____	Safety Meeting _____

Work Force	No.
Superintendent	_____
Clerk	_____
Bricklayers	_____
Carpenters	_____
Cement Masons	_____
Electricians	_____
Iron Workers	_____
Laborers	_____
Operating Eng.	_____
Plumbers	_____
Pipe Fitters	_____
Sheet Metal	_____
Truck Drivers	_____
Total	_____

Problems - Delays _____

Equipment	Hrs.

Sub-Contractor Progress _____

Special Assignments _____

Extra Work	Authorized By	Approx. Price

Equipment Rented Today	Rented From	Rate

Material Purchased

Supervisor's Signature _____

18 JULY 20___   DAILY LOG   DAY _____

CONTRACTOR _____ JOB NAME _____ JOB NO. _____

Work Performed Today _____	Weather _____
	Temp. AM _____ PM _____
	Safety Meeting _____

Work Force	No.
Superintendent	_____
Clerk	_____
Bricklayers	_____
Carpenters	_____
Cement Masons	_____
Electricians	_____
Iron Workers	_____
Laborers	_____
Operating Eng.	_____
Plumbers	_____
Pipe Fitters	_____
Sheet Metal	_____
Truck Drivers	_____
Total	_____

Problems - Delays _____

Sub-Contractor Progress _____

Equipment	Hrs.

Special Assignments _____

Extra Work	Authorized By	Approx. Price

Equipment Rented Today	Rented From	Rate

Material Purchased

Supervisor's Signature _____

DAY _____   DAILY LOG   20____ JULY 19

CONTRACTOR _____ JOB NAME _____ JOB NO _____

Work Performed Today _____

_____

_____

_____

_____

_____

_____

_____

_____

_____

_____

_____

_____

_____

Problems - Delays _____

_____

_____

_____

Sub-Contractor Progress _____

_____

_____

_____

Special Assignments _____

_____

_____

Weather	_____
Temp. AM _____ PM _____	
Safety Meeting _____	

Work Force	No.
Superintendent	_____
Clerk	_____
Bricklayers	_____
Carpenters	_____
Cement Masons	_____
Electricians	_____
Iron Workers	_____
Laborers	_____
Operating Eng.	_____
Plumbers	_____
Pipe Fitters	_____
Sheet Metal	_____
Truck Drivers	_____
Total	_____

Equipment	Hrs.

Extra Work	Authorized By	Approx. Price

Equipment Rented Today	Rented From	Rate

Material Purchased

Supervisor's Signature _____

20 JULY 20___ DAILY LOG DAY _____

CONTRACTOR _____ JOB NAME _____ JOB NO._____

Work Performed Today _____

_____

_____

_____

_____

_____

_____

_____

_____

_____

_____

_____

_____

_____

Problems - Delays _____

_____

_____

_____

Sub-Contractor Progress _____

_____

_____

_____

Special Assignments _____

_____

_____

_____

Weather	
Temp. AM _____PM _____	
Safety Meeting _____	

Work Force	No.
Superintendent	_____
Clerk	_____
Bricklayers	_____
Carpenters	_____
Cement Masons	_____
Electricians	_____
Iron Workers	_____
Laborers	_____
Operating Eng.	_____
Plumbers	_____
Pipe Fitters	_____
Sheet Metal	_____
Truck Drivers	_____
Total	_____

Equipment	Hrs.

Extra Work	Authorized By	Approx. Price

Equipment Rented Today	Rented From	Rate

Material Purchased

Supervisor's Signature _____

DAY _____   DAILY LOG   20___ JULY 21

CONTRACTOR _____ JOB NAME _____ JOB NO _____

Work Performed Today _____

_____

_____

_____

_____

_____

_____

_____

_____

_____

_____

_____

_____

_____

Problems - Delays _____

_____

_____

_____

Sub-Contractor Progress _____

_____

_____

_____

Special Assignments _____

_____

_____

| Weather _____ |
| Temp. AM _____ PM _____ |
| Safety Meeting _____ |

Work Force	No.
Superintendent	_____
Clerk	_____
Bricklayers	_____
Carpenters	_____
Cement Masons	_____
Electricians	_____
Iron Workers	_____
Laborers	_____
Operating Eng.	_____
Plumbers	_____
Pipe Fitters	_____
Sheet Metal	_____
Truck Drivers	_____
Total	_____

Equipment	Hrs.

Extra Work	Authorized By	Approx. Price

Equipment Rented Today	Rented From	Rate

Material Purchased

Supervisor's Signature _____

22 JULY 20___   DAILY LOG   DAY _____

CONTRACTOR _____ JOB NAME _____ JOB NO._____

Work Performed Today _____

_____

_____

_____

_____

_____

_____

_____

_____

_____

_____

_____

_____

_____

_____

_____

Problems - Delays _____

_____

_____

_____

Sub-Contractor Progress _____

_____

_____

_____

Special Assignments _____

_____

_____

Extra Work	Authorized By	Approx. Price

Equipment Rented Today	Rented From	Rate

Supervisor's Signature _____

Weather _____

Temp. AM _____ PM _____

Safety Meeting _____

Work Force	No.
Superintendent	_____
Clerk	_____
Bricklayers	_____
Carpenters	_____
Cement Masons	_____
Electricians	_____
Iron Workers	_____
Laborers	_____
Operating Eng.	_____
Plumbers	_____
Pipe Fitters	_____
Sheet Metal	_____
Truck Drivers	_____
Total	_____

Equipment	Hrs.

Material Purchased

DAY _____   DAILY LOG   20___ JULY 23

CONTRACTOR _____ JOB NAME _____ JOB NO _____

Work Performed Today _____	Weather _____
	Temp. AM _____PM _____

Work Performed Today _____

_____

_____

_____

_____

_____

_____

_____

_____

_____

_____

_____

_____

_____

_____

_____

Problems - Delays _____

_____

_____

_____

Sub-Contractor Progress _____

_____

_____

_____

Special Assignments _____

_____

_____

Weather _____

Temp. AM _____PM _____

Safety Meeting _____

Work Force	No.
Superintendent	_____
Clerk	_____
Bricklayers	_____
Carpenters	_____
Cement Masons	_____
Electricians	_____
Iron Workers	_____
Laborers	_____
Operating Eng.	_____
Plumbers	_____
Pipe Fitters	_____
Sheet Metal	_____
Truck Drivers	_____
Total	_____

Equipment	Hrs.

Extra Work	Authorized By	Approx. Price

Equipment Rented Today	Rented From	Rate

Material Purchased

Supervisor's Signature _____

24 JULY 20___   DAILY LOG   DAY _____

CONTRACTOR _____ JOB NAME _____ JOB NO._____

Work Performed Today _____

_____

_____

_____

_____

_____

_____

_____

_____

_____

_____

_____

Problems - Delays _____

_____

_____

_____

Sub-Contractor Progress _____

_____

_____

_____

Special Assignments _____

_____

_____

Extra Work	Authorized By	Approx. Price

Equipment Rented Today	Rented From	Rate

Supervisor's Signature _____

Weather _____

Temp. AM _____PM _____

Safety Meeting _____

Work Force	No.
Superintendent	_____
Clerk	_____
Bricklayers	_____
Carpenters	_____
Cement Masons	_____
Electricians	_____
Iron Workers	_____
Laborers	_____
Operating Eng.	_____
Plumbers	_____
Pipe Fitters	_____
Sheet Metal	_____
Truck Drivers	_____
Total	_____

Equipment	Hrs.

Material Purchased

DAY _____ DAILY LOG 20___ JULY 25

CONTRACTOR _____ JOB NAME _____ JOB NO _____

Work Performed Today _____	Weather _____
	Temp. AM _____PM _____
	Safety Meeting _____
	Work Force **No.**
	Superintendent _____
	Clerk _____
	Bricklayers _____
	Carpenters _____
	Cement Masons _____
	Electricians _____
	Iron Workers _____
	Laborers _____
	Operating Eng. _____
	Plumbers _____
	Pipe Fitters _____
	Sheet Metal _____
	Truck Drivers _____

Problems - Delays _____

| | **Total** _____ |

Sub-Contractor Progress _____

Equipment	Hrs.

Special Assignments _____

Material Purchased	

Extra Work	Authorized By	Approx. Price

Equipment Rented Today	Rented From	Rate

Supervisor's Signature _____

26 JULY 20___   DAILY LOG   DAY _____

CONTRACTOR _____ JOB NAME _____ JOB NO. _____

Work Performed Today _____

_____

_____

_____

_____

_____

_____

_____

_____

_____

_____

_____

_____

_____

_____

Problems - Delays _____

_____

_____

_____

Sub-Contractor Progress _____

_____

_____

_____

Special Assignments _____

_____

_____

| Weather _____ |
| Temp. AM _____ PM _____ |
| Safety Meeting _____ |

Work Force	No.
Superintendent	_____
Clerk	_____
Bricklayers	_____
Carpenters	_____
Cement Masons	_____
Electricians	_____
Iron Workers	_____
Laborers	_____
Operating Eng.	_____
Plumbers	_____
Pipe Fitters	_____
Sheet Metal	_____
Truck Drivers	_____
Total	_____

Equipment	Hrs.

Material Purchased

Extra Work	Authorized By	Approx. Price

Equipment Rented Today	Rented From	Rate

Supervisor's Signature _____

DAY _____   DAILY LOG   20___ JULY 27

CONTRACTOR _____ JOB NAME _____ JOB NO _____

Work Performed Today		Weather _____
		Temp. AM _____ PM _____
		Safety Meeting _____

Work Force	No.
Superintendent	_____
Clerk	_____
Bricklayers	_____
Carpenters	_____
Cement Masons	_____
Electricians	_____
Iron Workers	_____
Laborers	_____
Operating Eng.	_____
Plumbers	_____
Pipe Fitters	_____
Sheet Metal	_____
Truck Drivers	_____
Total	_____

Problems - Delays _____

Sub-Contractor Progress _____

Equipment	Hrs.

Special Assignments _____

Extra Work	Authorized By	Approx. Price

Equipment Rented Today	Rented From	Rate

Material Purchased

Supervisor's Signature _____

28 JULY 20___   DAILY LOG   DAY _____

CONTRACTOR _____ JOB NAME _____ JOB NO._____

Work Performed Today _____	Weather _____
	Temp. AM _____PM _____
	Safety Meeting _____

Work Force	No.
Superintendent	_____
Clerk	_____
Bricklayers	_____
Carpenters	_____
Cement Masons	_____
Electricians	_____
Iron Workers	_____
Laborers	_____
Operating Eng.	_____
Plumbers	_____
Pipe Fitters	_____
Sheet Metal	_____
Truck Drivers	_____
Total	_____

Problems - Delays _____

Equipment	Hrs.

Sub-Contractor Progress _____

Special Assignments _____

Material Purchased	

Extra Work	Authorized By	Approx. Price

Equipment Rented Today	Rented From	Rate

Supervisor's Signature _____

DAY _____   DAILY LOG   20____ JULY 29

CONTRACTOR _____ JOB NAME _____ JOB NO _____

Work Performed Today _____	Weather _____
	Temp. AM _____ PM _____
	Safety Meeting _____

Work Force	No.
Superintendent	_____
Clerk	_____
Bricklayers	_____
Carpenters	_____
Cement Masons	_____
Electricians	_____
Iron Workers	_____
Laborers	_____
Operating Eng.	_____
Plumbers	_____
Pipe Fitters	_____
Sheet Metal	_____
Truck Drivers	_____
Total	_____

Problems - Delays _____

Equipment	Hrs.

Sub-Contractor Progress _____

Special Assignments _____

Material Purchased

Extra Work	Authorized By	Approx. Price

Equipment Rented Today	Rented From	Rate

Supervisor's Signature _____

30 JULY 20____   DAILY LOG   DAY _____

CONTRACTOR _____ JOB NAME _____ JOB NO._____

Work Performed Today _____

_____

_____

_____

_____

_____

_____

_____

_____

_____

_____

_____

Problems - Delays _____

_____

_____

_____

Sub-Contractor Progress _____

_____

_____

_____

Special Assignments _____

_____

_____

| Weather _____ |
| Temp. AM _____ PM _____ |
| Safety Meeting _____ |

Work Force	No.
Superintendent	_____
Clerk	_____
Bricklayers	_____
Carpenters	_____
Cement Masons	_____
Electricians	_____
Iron Workers	_____
Laborers	_____
Operating Eng.	_____
Plumbers	_____
Pipe Fitters	_____
Sheet Metal	_____
Truck Drivers	_____
Total	_____

Equipment	Hrs.

Extra Work	Authorized By	Approx. Price

Equipment Rented Today	Rented From	Rate

Material Purchased

Supervisor's Signature _____

DAY _____   DAILY LOG   20____ JULY 31

CONTRACTOR _____ JOB NAME _____ JOB NO _____

Work Performed Today _____

_____

_____

_____

_____

_____

_____

_____

_____

_____

_____

_____

_____

_____

Problems - Delays _____

_____

_____

_____

Sub-Contractor Progress _____

_____

_____

Special Assignments _____

_____

_____

| Weather _____ |
| Temp. AM _____ PM _____ |
| Safety Meeting _____ |

Work Force	No.
Superintendent	_____
Clerk	_____
Bricklayers	_____
Carpenters	_____
Cement Masons	_____
Electricians	_____
Iron Workers	_____
Laborers	_____
Operating Eng.	_____
Plumbers	_____
Pipe Fitters	_____
Sheet Metal	_____
Truck Drivers	_____
Total	_____

Equipment	Hrs.

Material Purchased

Extra Work	Authorized By	Approx. Price

Equipment Rented Today	Rented From	Rate

Supervisor's Signature _____

1 AUG. 20___ DAILY LOG DAY _____

CONTRACTOR _____ JOB NAME _____ JOB NO._____

Work Performed Today _____	Weather_____
	Temp. AM _____PM _____
	Safety Meeting _____

Work Force	No.
Superintendent	_____
Clerk	_____
Bricklayers	_____
Carpenters	_____
Cement Masons	_____
Electricians	_____
Iron Workers	_____
Laborers	_____
Operating Eng.	_____
Plumbers	_____
Pipe Fitters	_____
Sheet Metal	_____
Truck Drivers	_____
Total	_____

Problems - Delays _____

Equipment	Hrs.

Sub-Contractor Progress _____

Special Assignments _____

Extra Work	Authorized By	Approx. Price

Equipment Rented Today	Rented From	Rate

Material Purchased

Supervisor's Signature _____

DAY _____   DAILY LOG   20___ AUG. 2

CONTRACTOR _____ JOB NAME _____ JOB NO _____

Work Performed Today _____	Weather _____
	Temp. AM _____ PM _____
	Safety Meeting _____

Work Force	No.
Superintendent	_____
Clerk	_____
Bricklayers	_____
Carpenters	_____
Cement Masons	_____
Electricians	_____
Iron Workers	_____
Laborers	_____
Operating Eng.	_____
Plumbers	_____
Pipe Fitters	_____
Sheet Metal	_____
Truck Drivers	_____
Total	_____

Problems - Delays _____

Equipment	Hrs.

Sub-Contractor Progress _____

Special Assignments _____

Extra Work	Authorized By	Approx. Price

Equipment Rented Today	Rented From	Rate

Material Purchased

Supervisor's Signature _____

3 AUG. 20___   DAILY LOG   DAY _____

CONTRACTOR _____ JOB NAME _____ JOB NO. _____

Work Performed Today _____

_____

_____

_____

_____

_____

_____

_____

_____

_____

_____

_____

_____

Problems - Delays _____

_____

_____

_____

Sub-Contractor Progress _____

_____

_____

Special Assignments _____

_____

_____

| Weather _____ |
| Temp. AM _____ PM _____ |
| Safety Meeting _____ |

Work Force	No.
Superintendent	_____
Clerk	_____
Bricklayers	_____
Carpenters	_____
Cement Masons	_____
Electricians	_____
Iron Workers	_____
Laborers	_____
Operating Eng.	_____
Plumbers	_____
Pipe Fitters	_____
Sheet Metal	_____
Truck Drivers	_____
Total	_____

Equipment	Hrs.

Material Purchased	

Extra Work	Authorized By	Approx. Price

Equipment Rented Today	Rented From	Rate

Supervisor's Signature _____

DAY _____   DAILY LOG   20___ AUG. 4

CONTRACTOR _____ JOB NAME _____ JOB NO _____

Work Performed Today _____

_____

_____

_____

_____

_____

_____

_____

_____

_____

_____

_____

_____

_____

Problems - Delays _____

_____

_____

_____

_____

Sub-Contractor Progress _____

_____

_____

_____

Special Assignments _____

_____

_____

Weather	_____
Temp. AM _____ PM _____	
Safety Meeting _____	

Work Force	No.
Superintendent	_____
Clerk	_____
Bricklayers	_____
Carpenters	_____
Cement Masons	_____
Electricians	_____
Iron Workers	_____
Laborers	_____
Operating Eng.	_____
Plumbers	_____
Pipe Fitters	_____
Sheet Metal	_____
Truck Drivers	_____
Total	_____

Equipment	Hrs.

Extra Work	Authorized By	Approx. Price

Equipment Rented Today	Rented From	Rate

Material Purchased

Supervisor's Signature _____

5 AUG. 20___　　　　DAILY LOG　　　　DAY _____

CONTRACTOR _____ JOB NAME _____ JOB NO._____

Work Performed Today _____	Weather_____
	Temp. AM _____PM _____
	Safety Meeting _____

Work Force	No.
Superintendent	_____
Clerk	_____
Bricklayers	_____
Carpenters	_____
Cement Masons	_____
Electricians	_____
Iron Workers	_____
Laborers	_____
Operating Eng.	_____
Plumbers	_____
Pipe Fitters	_____
Sheet Metal	_____
Truck Drivers	_____
Total	_____

Problems - Delays _____

Equipment	Hrs.

Sub-Contractor Progress _____

Special Assignments _____

Extra Work	Authorized By	Approx. Price

Equipment Rented Today	Rented From	Rate

Material Purchased

Supervisor's Signature _____

DAY _____   DAILY LOG   20___ AUG. 6

CONTRACTOR _____ JOB NAME _____ JOB NO _____

Work Performed Today _____

_____

_____

_____

_____

_____

_____

_____

_____

_____

_____

_____

_____

_____

Problems - Delays _____

_____

_____

_____

Sub-Contractor Progress _____

_____

_____

_____

Special Assignments _____

_____

_____

Weather		
Temp. AM _____ PM _____		
Safety Meeting _____		

Work Force	No.
Superintendent	_____
Clerk	_____
Bricklayers	_____
Carpenters	_____
Cement Masons	_____
Electricians	_____
Iron Workers	_____
Laborers	_____
Operating Eng.	_____
Plumbers	_____
Pipe Fitters	_____
Sheet Metal	_____
Truck Drivers	_____
Total	_____

Equipment	Hrs.

Extra Work	Authorized By	Approx. Price

Equipment Rented Today	Rented From	Rate

Material Purchased

Supervisor's Signature _____

7 AUG. 20___   DAILY LOG   DAY _____

CONTRACTOR _____ JOB NAME _____ JOB NO._____

Work Performed Today _____	Weather _____
	Temp. AM _____PM ____
	Safety Meeting _____

Work Force	No.
Superintendent	_____
Clerk	_____
Bricklayers	_____
Carpenters	_____
Cement Masons	_____
Electricians	_____
Iron Workers	_____
Laborers	_____
Operating Eng.	_____
Plumbers	_____
Pipe Fitters	_____
Sheet Metal	_____
Truck Drivers	_____
Total	_____

Problems - Delays _____

Sub-Contractor Progress _____

Special Assignments _____

Equipment	Hrs.

Extra Work	Authorized By	Approx. Price

Equipment Rented Today	Rented From	Rate

Material Purchased

Supervisor's Signature _____

DAY _____   DAILY LOG   20___ AUG. 8

CONTRACTOR _____ JOB NAME _____ JOB NO _____

Work Performed Today _____

_____

_____

_____

_____

_____

_____

_____

_____

_____

_____

_____

_____

_____

Problems - Delays _____

_____

_____

_____

Sub-Contractor Progress _____

_____

_____

_____

Special Assignments _____

_____

_____

| Weather _____ |
| Temp. AM _____ PM _____ |
| Safety Meeting _____ |

Work Force	No.
Superintendent	_____
Clerk	_____
Bricklayers	_____
Carpenters	_____
Cement Masons	_____
Electricians	_____
Iron Workers	_____
Laborers	_____
Operating Eng.	_____
Plumbers	_____
Pipe Fitters	_____
Sheet Metal	_____
Truck Drivers	_____
Total	_____

Equipment	Hrs.

Material Purchased	

Extra Work	Authorized By	Approx. Price

Equipment Rented Today	Rented From	Rate

Supervisor's Signature _____

9 AUG. 20___   DAILY LOG   DAY _____

CONTRACTOR _____ JOB NAME _____ JOB NO._____

Work Performed Today _____	Weather _____
_____	Temp. AM _____PM _____
_____	Safety Meeting _____
_____	**Work Force** **No.**

Work Performed Today _____

_____

_____

_____

_____

_____

_____

_____

_____

_____

_____

_____

_____

_____

Problems - Delays _____

_____

_____

_____

Sub-Contractor Progress _____

_____

_____

Special Assignments _____

_____

_____

Weather _____

Temp. AM _____PM _____

Safety Meeting _____

Work Force	No.
Superintendent	_____
Clerk	_____
Bricklayers	_____
Carpenters	_____
Cement Masons	_____
Electricians	_____
Iron Workers	_____
Laborers	_____
Operating Eng.	_____
Plumbers	_____
Pipe Fitters	_____
Sheet Metal	_____
Truck Drivers	_____
Total	_____

Equipment	Hrs.

Extra Work	Authorized By	Approx. Price

Equipment Rented Today	Rented From	Rate

Material Purchased

Supervisor's Signature _____

DAY _____   DAILY LOG   20___ AUG. 10

CONTRACTOR _____ JOB NAME _____ JOB NO _____

Work Performed Today _____

_____

_____

_____

_____

_____

_____

_____

_____

_____

_____

_____

_____

_____

_____

Problems - Delays _____

_____

_____

_____

Sub-Contractor Progress _____

_____

_____

_____

Special Assignments _____

_____

_____

Weather		_____
Temp. AM _____ PM _____		
Safety Meeting _____		

Work Force	No.
Superintendent	_____
Clerk	_____
Bricklayers	_____
Carpenters	_____
Cement Masons	_____
Electricians	_____
Iron Workers	_____
Laborers	_____
Operating Eng.	_____
Plumbers	_____
Pipe Fitters	_____
Sheet Metal	_____
Truck Drivers	_____
Total	_____

Equipment	Hrs.

Material Purchased	

Extra Work	Authorized By	Approx. Price

Equipment Rented Today	Rented From	Rate

Supervisor's Signature _____

11 AUG. 20___   DAILY LOG   DAY _____

CONTRACTOR _____ JOB NAME _____ JOB NO._____

Work Performed Today _____	Weather _____
	Temp. AM _____PM _____
	Safety Meeting _____

Work Force	No.
Superintendent	_____
Clerk	_____
Bricklayers	_____
Carpenters	_____
Cement Masons	_____
Electricians	_____
Iron Workers	_____
Laborers	_____
Operating Eng.	_____
Plumbers	_____
Pipe Fitters	_____
Sheet Metal	_____
Truck Drivers	_____
Total	_____

Problems - Delays _____

Sub-Contractor Progress _____

Equipment	Hrs.

Special Assignments _____

Extra Work	Authorized By	Approx. Price

Equipment Rented Today	Rented From	Rate

Material Purchased

Supervisor's Signature _____

DAY _____   DAILY LOG   20___ AUG. 12

CONTRACTOR _____ JOB NAME _____ JOB NO _____

Work Performed Today _____

_____

_____

_____

_____

_____

_____

_____

_____

_____

_____

_____

_____

Problems - Delays _____

_____

_____

_____

Sub-Contractor Progress _____

_____

_____

_____

Special Assignments _____

_____

_____

| Weather _____ |
| Temp. AM ____ PM ____ |
| Safety Meeting _____ |

Work Force	No.
Superintendent	____
Clerk	____
Bricklayers	____
Carpenters	____
Cement Masons	____
Electricians	____
Iron Workers	____
Laborers	____
Operating Eng.	____
Plumbers	____
Pipe Fitters	____
Sheet Metal	____
Truck Drivers	____
Total	____

Equipment	Hrs.

Extra Work	Authorized By	Approx. Price

Equipment Rented Today	Rented From	Rate

Material Purchased

Supervisor's Signature _____

13 AUG. 20___   DAILY LOG   DAY _____

CONTRACTOR _____ JOB NAME _____ JOB NO._____

Work Performed Today _____	Weather _____
_____	Temp. AM _____ PM _____
_____	Safety Meeting _____

Work Force	No.
Superintendent	_____
Clerk	_____
Bricklayers	_____
Carpenters	_____
Cement Masons	_____
Electricians	_____
Iron Workers	_____
Laborers	_____
Operating Eng.	_____
Plumbers	_____
Pipe Fitters	_____
Sheet Metal	_____
Truck Drivers	_____
Total	_____

Work Performed Today _____

_____

_____

_____

_____

_____

_____

_____

_____

_____

_____

_____

_____

Problems - Delays _____

_____

_____

_____

Sub-Contractor Progress _____

_____

_____

_____

Equipment	Hrs.

Special Assignments _____

_____

_____

Material Purchased	

Extra Work	Authorized By	Approx. Price

Equipment Rented Today	Rented From	Rate

Supervisor's Signature _____

DAY _____   DAILY LOG   20___ AUG. 14

CONTRACTOR _____ JOB NAME _____ JOB NO _____

Work Performed Today _____

_____

_____

_____

_____

_____

_____

_____

_____

_____

_____

_____

_____

_____

Problems - Delays _____

_____

_____

_____

Sub-Contractor Progress _____

_____

_____

_____

Special Assignments _____

_____

_____

Weather	_____
Temp. AM _____ PM _____	
Safety Meeting _____	

Work Force	No.
Superintendent	_____
Clerk	_____
Bricklayers	_____
Carpenters	_____
Cement Masons	_____
Electricians	_____
Iron Workers	_____
Laborers	_____
Operating Eng.	_____
Plumbers	_____
Pipe Fitters	_____
Sheet Metal	_____
Truck Drivers	_____
Total	_____

Equipment	Hrs.

Extra Work	Authorized By	Approx. Price

Equipment Rented Today	Rented From	Rate

Material Purchased

Supervisor's Signature _____

15 AUG. 20___   DAILY LOG   DAY _____

CONTRACTOR _____ JOB NAME _____ JOB NO. _____

Work Performed Today _____	Weather _____
_____	Temp. AM _____ PM _____
_____	Safety Meeting _____
_____	**Work Force** **No.**

Work Force	No.
Superintendent	_____
Clerk	_____
Bricklayers	_____
Carpenters	_____
Cement Masons	_____
Electricians	_____
Iron Workers	_____
Laborers	_____
Operating Eng.	_____
Plumbers	_____
Pipe Fitters	_____
Sheet Metal	_____
Truck Drivers	_____
Total	_____

Problems - Delays _____
_____
_____
_____

Sub-Contractor Progress _____
_____
_____
_____

Special Assignments _____
_____

Equipment	Hrs.

Extra Work	Authorized By	Approx. Price

Equipment Rented Today	Rented From	Rate

Material Purchased

Supervisor's Signature _____

DAY _____   DAILY LOG   20___ AUG. 16

CONTRACTOR _____ JOB NAME _____ JOB NO _____

Work Performed Today _____

_____

_____

_____

_____

_____

_____

_____

_____

_____

_____

_____

Problems - Delays _____

_____

_____

_____

Sub-Contractor Progress _____

_____

_____

_____

Special Assignments _____

_____

_____

Extra Work	Authorized By	Approx. Price

Equipment Rented Today	Rented From	Rate

Supervisor's Signature _____

Weather _____

Temp. AM _____PM _____

Safety Meeting _____

Work Force	No.
Superintendent	_____
Clerk	_____
Bricklayers	_____
Carpenters	_____
Cement Masons	_____
Electricians	_____
Iron Workers	_____
Laborers	_____
Operating Eng.	_____
Plumbers	_____
Pipe Fitters	_____
Sheet Metal	_____
Truck Drivers	_____
Total	_____

Equipment	Hrs.

Material Purchased

17 AUG. 20___   DAILY LOG   DAY _____

CONTRACTOR _____ JOB NAME _____ JOB NO._____

Work Performed Today _____

_____

_____

_____

_____

_____

_____

_____

_____

_____

_____

_____

_____

_____

Problems - Delays _____

_____

_____

_____

Sub-Contractor Progress _____

_____

_____

_____

Special Assignments _____

_____

_____

| Weather _____ |
| Temp. AM _____PM _____ |
| Safety Meeting _____ |

Work Force	No.
Superintendent	_____
Clerk	_____
Bricklayers	_____
Carpenters	_____
Cement Masons	_____
Electricians	_____
Iron Workers	_____
Laborers	_____
Operating Eng.	_____
Plumbers	_____
Pipe Fitters	_____
Sheet Metal	_____
Truck Drivers	_____
Total	_____

Equipment	Hrs.

Extra Work	Authorized By	Approx. Price

Equipment Rented Today	Rented From	Rate

Material Purchased

Supervisor's Signature _____

DAY _____   DAILY LOG   20___ AUG. 18

CONTRACTOR _____ JOB NAME _____ JOB NO _____

Work Performed Today _____

_____

_____

_____

_____

_____

_____

_____

_____

_____

_____

_____

_____

_____

_____

Problems - Delays _____

_____

_____

_____

_____

Sub-Contractor Progress _____

_____

_____

_____

Special Assignments _____

_____

_____

| Weather _____ |
| Temp. AM _____PM _____ |
| Safety Meeting _____ |

Work Force	No.
Superintendent	_____
Clerk	_____
Bricklayers	_____
Carpenters	_____
Cement Masons	_____
Electricians	_____
Iron Workers	_____
Laborers	_____
Operating Eng.	_____
Plumbers	_____
Pipe Fitters	_____
Sheet Metal	_____
Truck Drivers	_____
Total	_____

Equipment	Hrs.

Extra Work	Authorized By	Approx. Price

Equipment Rented Today	Rented From	Rate

Material Purchased

Supervisor's Signature _____

19 AUG. 20___   DAILY LOG   DAY _____

CONTRACTOR _____ JOB NAME _____ JOB NO._____

Work Performed Today _____	Weather _____
	Temp. AM _____ PM _____
	Safety Meeting _____

Work Force	**No.**
Superintendent	_____
Clerk	_____
Bricklayers	_____
Carpenters	_____
Cement Masons	_____
Electricians	_____
Iron Workers	_____
Laborers	_____
Operating Eng.	_____
Plumbers	_____
Pipe Fitters	_____
Sheet Metal	_____
Truck Drivers	_____
Total	_____

Problems - Delays _____

Equipment	Hrs.

Sub-Contractor Progress _____

Special Assignments _____

Material Purchased	

Extra Work	Authorized By	Approx. Price

Equipment Rented Today	Rented From	Rate

Supervisor's Signature _____

DAY _____   DAILY LOG   20___ AUG. 20

CONTRACTOR _____ JOB NAME _____ JOB NO _____

Work Performed Today _____

_____

_____

_____

_____

_____

_____

_____

_____

_____

_____

_____

_____

Problems - Delays _____

_____

_____

_____

Sub-Contractor Progress _____

_____

_____

_____

Special Assignments _____

_____

_____

| Weather | _____ |
| Temp. AM _____ PM _____ |
| Safety Meeting _____ |

Work Force	No.
Superintendent	_____
Clerk	_____
Bricklayers	_____
Carpenters	_____
Cement Masons	_____
Electricians	_____
Iron Workers	_____
Laborers	_____
Operating Eng.	_____
Plumbers	_____
Pipe Fitters	_____
Sheet Metal	_____
Truck Drivers	_____
Total	_____

Equipment	Hrs.

Extra Work	Authorized By	Approx. Price

Equipment Rented Today	Rented From	Rate

Material Purchased

Supervisor's Signature _____

21 AUG. 20___   DAILY LOG   DAY _____

CONTRACTOR _____ JOB NAME _____ JOB NO._____

Work Performed Today _____

_____

_____

_____

_____

_____

_____

_____

_____

_____

_____

_____

_____

Problems - Delays _____

_____

_____

_____

Sub-Contractor Progress _____

_____

_____

_____

Special Assignments _____

_____

_____

Weather	_____
Temp. AM _____ PM _____	
Safety Meeting _____	

Work Force	No.
Superintendent	_____
Clerk	_____
Bricklayers	_____
Carpenters	_____
Cement Masons	_____
Electricians	_____
Iron Workers	_____
Laborers	_____
Operating Eng.	_____
Plumbers	_____
Pipe Fitters	_____
Sheet Metal	_____
Truck Drivers	_____
Total	_____

Equipment	Hrs.

Extra Work	Authorized By	Approx. Price

Equipment Rented Today	Rented From	Rate

Material Purchased

Supervisor's Signature _____

DAY _____   DAILY LOG   20___ AUG. 22

CONTRACTOR _____ JOB NAME _____ JOB NO _____

Work Performed Today _____

_____

_____

_____

_____

_____

_____

_____

_____

_____

_____

_____

_____

Problems - Delays _____

_____

_____

_____

Sub-Contractor Progress _____

_____

_____

_____

Special Assignments _____

_____

_____

Extra Work	Authorized By	Approx. Price

Equipment Rented Today	Rented From	Rate

Supervisor's Signature _____

Weather _____

Temp. AM _____ PM _____

Safety Meeting _____

Work Force	No.
Superintendent	_____
Clerk	_____
Bricklayers	_____
Carpenters	_____
Cement Masons	_____
Electricians	_____
Iron Workers	_____
Laborers	_____
Operating Eng.	_____
Plumbers	_____
Pipe Fitters	_____
Sheet Metal	_____
Truck Drivers	_____
Total	_____

Equipment	Hrs.

Material Purchased

23 AUG. 20___   DAILY LOG   DAY _____

CONTRACTOR _____ JOB NAME _____ JOB NO._____

Work Performed Today _____	Weather _____
_____	Temp. AM _____PM _____
_____	Safety Meeting _____

Work Force	No.
Superintendent	_____
Clerk	_____
Bricklayers	_____
Carpenters	_____
Cement Masons	_____
Electricians	_____
Iron Workers	_____
Laborers	_____
Operating Eng.	_____
Plumbers	_____
Pipe Fitters	_____
Sheet Metal	_____
Truck Drivers	_____
Total	_____

Problems - Delays _____

Sub-Contractor Progress _____

Equipment	Hrs.

Special Assignments _____

Extra Work	Authorized By	Approx. Price

Equipment Rented Today	Rented From	Rate

Material Purchased

Supervisor's Signature _____

DAY _____   DAILY LOG   20___ AUG. 24

CONTRACTOR _____ JOB NAME _____ JOB NO _____

Work Performed Today _____

_____

_____

_____

_____

_____

_____

_____

_____

_____

_____

_____

Problems - Delays _____

_____

_____

_____

Sub-Contractor Progress _____

_____

_____

_____

Special Assignments _____

_____

_____

| Weather | _____ |

| Temp. AM _____ PM _____ |

| Safety Meeting _____ |

Work Force	No.
Superintendent	_____
Clerk	_____
Bricklayers	_____
Carpenters	_____
Cement Masons	_____
Electricians	_____
Iron Workers	_____
Laborers	_____
Operating Eng.	_____
Plumbers	_____
Pipe Fitters	_____
Sheet Metal	_____
Truck Drivers	_____
Total	_____

Equipment	Hrs.

Material Purchased

Extra Work	Authorized By	Approx. Price

Equipment Rented Today	Rented From	Rate

Supervisor's Signature _____

25 AUG. 20___   DAILY LOG   DAY _____

CONTRACTOR _____ JOB NAME _____ JOB NO. _____

Work Performed Today _____

_____

_____

_____

_____

_____

_____

_____

_____

_____

_____

_____

_____

_____

_____

_____

Problems - Delays _____

_____

_____

_____

Sub-Contractor Progress _____

_____

_____

_____

Special Assignments _____

_____

_____

Weather	_____
Temp. AM _____ PM _____	
Safety Meeting _____	

Work Force	No.
Superintendent	_____
Clerk	_____
Bricklayers	_____
Carpenters	_____
Cement Masons	_____
Electricians	_____
Iron Workers	_____
Laborers	_____
Operating Eng.	_____
Plumbers	_____
Pipe Fitters	_____
Sheet Metal	_____
Truck Drivers	_____
Total	_____

Equipment	Hrs.

Extra Work	Authorized By	Approx. Price

Equipment Rented Today	Rented From	Rate

Material Purchased

Supervisor's Signature _____

DAY _____   DAILY LOG   20___ AUG. 26

CONTRACTOR _____ JOB NAME _____ JOB NO _____

Work Performed Today _____

_____

_____

_____

_____

_____

_____

_____

_____

_____

_____

_____

_____

_____

_____

_____

Problems - Delays _____

_____

_____

_____

Sub-Contractor Progress _____

_____

_____

_____

Special Assignments _____

_____

_____

Extra Work	Authorized By	Approx. Price

Equipment Rented Today	Rented From	Rate

Supervisor's Signature _____

Weather _____

Temp. AM _____PM _____

Safety Meeting _____

Work Force	No.
Superintendent	_____
Clerk	_____
Bricklayers	_____
Carpenters	_____
Cement Masons	_____
Electricians	_____
Iron Workers	_____
Laborers	_____
Operating Eng.	_____
Plumbers	_____
Pipe Fitters	_____
Sheet Metal	_____
Truck Drivers	_____
Total	_____

Equipment	Hrs.

Material Purchased

27 AUG. 20___   DAILY LOG   DAY _____

CONTRACTOR _____ JOB NAME _____ JOB NO._____

Work Performed Today _____

_____

_____

_____

_____

_____

_____

_____

_____

_____

_____

_____

_____

_____

Problems - Delays _____

_____

_____

_____

Sub-Contractor Progress _____

_____

_____

Special Assignments _____

_____

_____

Extra Work	Authorized By	Approx. Price

Equipment Rented Today	Rented From	Rate

Supervisor's Signature _____

Weather _____

Temp. AM _____PM _____

Safety Meeting _____

Work Force	No.
Superintendent	_____
Clerk	_____
Bricklayers	_____
Carpenters	_____
Cement Masons	_____
Electricians	_____
Iron Workers	_____
Laborers	_____
Operating Eng.	_____
Plumbers	_____
Pipe Fitters	_____
Sheet Metal	_____
Truck Drivers	_____
Total	_____

Equipment	Hrs.

Material Purchased

DAY _____   DAILY LOG   20___ AUG. 28

CONTRACTOR _____ JOB NAME _____ JOB NO _____

Work Performed Today _____

_____

_____

_____

_____

_____

_____

_____

_____

_____

_____

_____

_____

_____

Problems - Delays _____

_____

_____

_____

Sub-Contractor Progress _____

_____

_____

_____

Special Assignments _____

_____

_____

Extra Work	Authorized By	Approx. Price

Equipment Rented Today	Rented From	Rate

Supervisor's Signature _____

Weather _____

Temp. AM _____ PM _____

Safety Meeting _____

Work Force	No.
Superintendent	_____
Clerk	_____
Bricklayers	_____
Carpenters	_____
Cement Masons	_____
Electricians	_____
Iron Workers	_____
Laborers	_____
Operating Eng.	_____
Plumbers	_____
Pipe Fitters	_____
Sheet Metal	_____
Truck Drivers	_____
Total	_____

Equipment	Hrs.

Material Purchased

29 AUG. 20___ DAILY LOG DAY _____

CONTRACTOR _____ JOB NAME _____ JOB NO._____

Work Performed Today _____	Weather _____
	Temp. AM _____PM _____
	Safety Meeting _____

Work Force	No.
Superintendent	_____
Clerk	_____
Bricklayers	_____
Carpenters	_____
Cement Masons	_____
Electricians	_____
Iron Workers	_____
Laborers	_____
Operating Eng.	_____
Plumbers	_____
Pipe Fitters	_____
Sheet Metal	_____
Truck Drivers	_____
Total	_____

Problems - Delays _____

Equipment	Hrs.

Sub-Contractor Progress _____

Special Assignments _____

Extra Work	Authorized By	Approx. Price

Equipment Rented Today	Rented From	Rate

Material Purchased

Supervisor's Signature _____

DAY _____   DAILY LOG   20____ AUG. 30

CONTRACTOR _____ JOB NAME _____ JOB NO _____

Work Performed Today _____

_____

_____

_____

_____

_____

_____

_____

_____

_____

_____

_____

_____

Problems - Delays _____

_____

_____

_____

Sub-Contractor Progress _____

_____

_____

_____

Special Assignments _____

_____

_____

| Weather _____ |
| Temp. AM _____PM _____ |
| Safety Meeting _____ |

Work Force	No.
Superintendent	_____
Clerk	_____
Bricklayers	_____
Carpenters	_____
Cement Masons	_____
Electricians	_____
Iron Workers	_____
Laborers	_____
Operating Eng.	_____
Plumbers	_____
Pipe Fitters	_____
Sheet Metal	_____
Truck Drivers	_____
Total	_____

Equipment	Hrs.

Extra Work	Authorized By	Approx. Price

Equipment Rented Today	Rented From	Rate

Material Purchased

Supervisor's Signature _____

31 AUG. 20___   DAILY LOG   DAY _____

CONTRACTOR _____ JOB NAME _____ JOB NO._____

Work Performed Today _____

_____

_____

_____

_____

_____

_____

_____

_____

_____

_____

_____

_____

_____

Problems - Delays _____

_____

_____

_____

Sub-Contractor Progress _____

_____

_____

_____

Special Assignments _____

_____

_____

_____

Weather	_____
Temp. AM _____ PM _____	
Safety Meeting _____	

Work Force	No.
Superintendent	_____
Clerk	_____
Bricklayers	_____
Carpenters	_____
Cement Masons	_____
Electricians	_____
Iron Workers	_____
Laborers	_____
Operating Eng.	_____
Plumbers	_____
Pipe Fitters	_____
Sheet Metal	_____
Truck Drivers	_____
Total	_____

Equipment	Hrs.

Extra Work	Authorized By	Approx. Price

Equipment Rented Today	Rented From	Rate

Material Purchased

Supervisor's Signature _____

DAY _____   DAILY LOG   20___ SEPT. 1

CONTRACTOR _____ JOB NAME _____ JOB NO _____

Work Performed Today _____	Weather _____

Work Performed Today _____

_____

_____

_____

_____

_____

_____

_____

_____

_____

_____

_____

_____

_____

Weather _____

Temp. AM _____ PM _____

Safety Meeting _____

Work Force	No.
Superintendent	_____
Clerk	_____
Bricklayers	_____
Carpenters	_____
Cement Masons	_____
Electricians	_____
Iron Workers	_____
Laborers	_____
Operating Eng.	_____
Plumbers	_____
Pipe Fitters	_____
Sheet Metal	_____
Truck Drivers	_____
Total	_____

Problems - Delays _____

_____

_____

_____

Sub-Contractor Progress _____

_____

_____

_____

Special Assignments _____

_____

_____

Equipment	Hrs.

Extra Work	Authorized By	Approx. Price

Equipment Rented Today	Rented From	Rate

Material Purchased

Supervisor's Signature _____

2 SEPT. 20___   DAILY LOG   DAY _____

CONTRACTOR _____ JOB NAME _____ JOB NO. _____

Work Performed Today _____

_____

_____

_____

_____

_____

_____

_____

_____

_____

_____

_____

_____

_____

Problems - Delays _____

_____

_____

_____

Sub-Contractor Progress _____

_____

_____

_____

Special Assignments _____

_____

_____

Weather	_____
Temp. AM _____ PM _____	
Safety Meeting _____	

Work Force	No.
Superintendent	_____
Clerk	_____
Bricklayers	_____
Carpenters	_____
Cement Masons	_____
Electricians	_____
Iron Workers	_____
Laborers	_____
Operating Eng.	_____
Plumbers	_____
Pipe Fitters	_____
Sheet Metal	_____
Truck Drivers	_____
Total	_____

Equipment	Hrs.

Extra Work	Authorized By	Approx. Price

Equipment Rented Today	Rented From	Rate

Material Purchased

Supervisor's Signature _____

DAY _____   DAILY LOG   20___ SEPT. 3

CONTRACTOR _____ JOB NAME _____ JOB NO _____

Work Performed Today _____	Weather _____
_____	Temp. AM _____ PM _____
_____	Safety Meeting _____

Work Force	No.
Superintendent	_____
Clerk	_____
Bricklayers	_____
Carpenters	_____
Cement Masons	_____
Electricians	_____
Iron Workers	_____
Laborers	_____
Operating Eng.	_____
Plumbers	_____
Pipe Fitters	_____
Sheet Metal	_____
Truck Drivers	_____
Total	_____

Problems - Delays _____

Equipment	Hrs.

Sub-Contractor Progress _____

Special Assignments _____

Extra Work	Authorized By	Approx. Price

Equipment Rented Today	Rented From	Rate

Material Purchased

Supervisor's Signature _____

4 SEPT. 20___   DAILY LOG   DAY _____

CONTRACTOR _____ JOB NAME _____ JOB NO._____

Work Performed Today _____

_____

_____

_____

_____

_____

_____

_____

_____

_____

_____

_____

_____

_____

Problems - Delays _____

_____

_____

_____

_____

Sub-Contractor Progress _____

_____

_____

_____

Special Assignments _____

_____

_____

_____

Extra Work	Authorized By	Approx. Price

Equipment Rented Today	Rented From	Rate

Supervisor's Signature _____

Weather _____

Temp. AM _____ PM _____

Safety Meeting _____

Work Force	No.
Superintendent	_____
Clerk	_____
Bricklayers	_____
Carpenters	_____
Cement Masons	_____
Electricians	_____
Iron Workers	_____
Laborers	_____
Operating Eng.	_____
Plumbers	_____
Pipe Fitters	_____
Sheet Metal	_____
Truck Drivers	_____
Total	_____

Equipment	Hrs.

Material Purchased

DAY _____   DAILY LOG   20___ SEPT. 5

CONTRACTOR _____ JOB NAME _____ JOB NO _____

Work Performed Today _____

_____

_____

_____

_____

_____

_____

_____

_____

_____

_____

_____

_____

_____

_____

Problems - Delays _____

_____

_____

_____

Sub-Contractor Progress _____

_____

_____

_____

Special Assignments _____

_____

_____

_____

Extra Work	Authorized By	Approx. Price

Equipment Rented Today	Rented From	Rate

Supervisor's Signature _____

Weather _____

Temp. AM _____ PM _____

Safety Meeting _____

Work Force	No.
Superintendent	_____
Clerk	_____
Bricklayers	_____
Carpenters	_____
Cement Masons	_____
Electricians	_____
Iron Workers	_____
Laborers	_____
Operating Eng.	_____
Plumbers	_____
Pipe Fitters	_____
Sheet Metal	_____
Truck Drivers	_____
Total	_____

Equipment	Hrs.

Material Purchased

6 SEPT. 20___   DAILY LOG   DAY _____

CONTRACTOR _____ JOB NAME _____ JOB NO. _____

Work Performed Today _____

_____

_____

_____

_____

_____

_____

_____

_____

_____

_____

_____

_____

_____

Problems - Delays _____

_____

_____

_____

Sub-Contractor Progress _____

_____

_____

_____

Special Assignments _____

_____

_____

| Weather _____ |
| Temp. AM _____ PM _____ |
| Safety Meeting _____ |

Work Force	No.
Superintendent	_____
Clerk	_____
Bricklayers	_____
Carpenters	_____
Cement Masons	_____
Electricians	_____
Iron Workers	_____
Laborers	_____
Operating Eng.	_____
Plumbers	_____
Pipe Fitters	_____
Sheet Metal	_____
Truck Drivers	_____
Total	_____

Equipment	Hrs.

Material Purchased	

Extra Work	Authorized By	Approx. Price

Equipment Rented Today	Rented From	Rate

Supervisor's Signature _____

DAY _____   DAILY LOG   20____ SEPT. 7

CONTRACTOR _____ JOB NAME _____ JOB NO _____

Work Performed Today _____	Weather _____
	Temp. AM _____PM _____

Safety Meeting _____

Work Force	No.
Superintendent	_____
Clerk	_____
Bricklayers	_____
Carpenters	_____
Cement Masons	_____
Electricians	_____
Iron Workers	_____
Laborers	_____
Operating Eng.	_____
Plumbers	_____
Pipe Fitters	_____
Sheet Metal	_____
Truck Drivers	_____
Total	_____

Problems - Delays _____

Equipment	Hrs.

Sub-Contractor Progress _____

Special Assignments _____

Material Purchased

Extra Work	Authorized By	Approx. Price

Equipment Rented Today	Rented From	Rate

Supervisor's Signature _____

8 SEPT. 20___   DAILY LOG   DAY _____

CONTRACTOR _____ JOB NAME _____ JOB NO._____

Work Performed Today _____	Weather _____
	Temp. AM _____ PM _____
	Safety Meeting _____

Work Force	No.
Superintendent	_____
Clerk	_____
Bricklayers	_____
Carpenters	_____
Cement Masons	_____
Electricians	_____
Iron Workers	_____
Laborers	_____
Operating Eng.	_____
Plumbers	_____
Pipe Fitters	_____
Sheet Metal	_____
Truck Drivers	_____
Total	_____

Problems - Delays _____

Sub-Contractor Progress _____

Equipment	Hrs.

Special Assignments _____

Extra Work	Authorized By	Approx. Price

Equipment Rented Today	Rented From	Rate

Material Purchased

Supervisor's Signature _____

DAY _____   DAILY LOG   20___ SEPT. 9

CONTRACTOR _____ JOB NAME _____ JOB NO _____

Work Performed Today	Weather _____

Temp. AM _____PM _____

Safety Meeting _____

Work Force	No.
Superintendent	_____
Clerk	_____
Bricklayers	_____
Carpenters	_____
Cement Masons	_____
Electricians	_____
Iron Workers	_____
Laborers	_____
Operating Eng.	_____
Plumbers	_____
Pipe Fitters	_____
Sheet Metal	_____
Truck Drivers	_____
Total	_____

Problems - Delays _____

Equipment	Hrs.

Sub-Contractor Progress _____

Special Assignments _____

Extra Work	Authorized By	Approx. Price

Equipment Rented Today	Rented From	Rate

Material Purchased

Supervisor's Signature _____

10 SEPT. 20___   DAILY LOG   DAY _____

CONTRACTOR _____ JOB NAME _____ JOB NO._____

Work Performed Today _____

_____

_____

_____

_____

_____

_____

_____

_____

_____

_____

_____

_____

_____

_____

_____

Problems - Delays _____

_____

_____

_____

Sub-Contractor Progress _____

_____

_____

_____

Special Assignments _____

_____

_____

Weather	_____
Temp. AM _____ PM _____	
Safety Meeting _____	

Work Force	No.
Superintendent	_____
Clerk	_____
Bricklayers	_____
Carpenters	_____
Cement Masons	_____
Electricians	_____
Iron Workers	_____
Laborers	_____
Operating Eng.	_____
Plumbers	_____
Pipe Fitters	_____
Sheet Metal	_____
Truck Drivers	_____
Total	_____

Equipment	Hrs.

Extra Work	Authorized By	Approx. Price

Equipment Rented Today	Rented From	Rate

Material Purchased

Supervisor's Signature _____

DAY _____   DAILY LOG   20___ SEPT. 11

CONTRACTOR _____ JOB NAME _____ JOB NO _____

Work Performed Today _____

_____

_____

_____

_____

_____

_____

_____

_____

_____

_____

_____

_____

_____

Problems - Delays _____

_____

_____

_____

Sub-Contractor Progress _____

_____

_____

_____

Special Assignments _____

_____

_____

| Weather _____ |
| Temp. AM _____PM _____ |
| Safety Meeting _____ |

Work Force	No.
Superintendent	_____
Clerk	_____
Bricklayers	_____
Carpenters	_____
Cement Masons	_____
Electricians	_____
Iron Workers	_____
Laborers	_____
Operating Eng.	_____
Plumbers	_____
Pipe Fitters	_____
Sheet Metal	_____
Truck Drivers	_____
Total	_____

Equipment	Hrs.

Extra Work	Authorized By	Approx. Price

Equipment Rented Today	Rented From	Rate

Material Purchased

Supervisor's Signature _____

12 SEPT. 20___   DAILY LOG   DAY _____

CONTRACTOR _____ JOB NAME _____ JOB NO._____

Work Performed Today _____

_____

_____

_____

_____

_____

_____

_____

_____

_____

_____

_____

_____

_____

_____

Problems - Delays _____

_____

_____

_____

Sub-Contractor Progress _____

_____

_____

Special Assignments _____

_____

_____

Weather	_____
Temp. AM _____ PM _____	
Safety Meeting _____	

Work Force	No.
Superintendent	_____
Clerk	_____
Bricklayers	_____
Carpenters	_____
Cement Masons	_____
Electricians	_____
Iron Workers	_____
Laborers	_____
Operating Eng.	_____
Plumbers	_____
Pipe Fitters	_____
Sheet Metal	_____
Truck Drivers	_____
Total	_____

Equipment	Hrs.

Material Purchased	

Extra Work	Authorized By	Approx. Price

Equipment Rented Today	Rented From	Rate

Supervisor's Signature _____

DAY _____   DAILY LOG   20___ SEPT. 13

CONTRACTOR _____ JOB NAME _____ JOB NO _____

Work Performed Today _____	Weather _____
	Temp. AM _____PM _____
	Safety Meeting _____

Work Force	**No.**
Superintendent	_____
Clerk	_____
Bricklayers	_____
Carpenters	_____
Cement Masons	_____
Electricians	_____
Iron Workers	_____
Laborers	_____
Operating Eng.	_____
Plumbers	_____
Pipe Fitters	_____
Sheet Metal	_____
Truck Drivers	_____
Total	_____

Problems - Delays _____

Equipment	Hrs.

Sub-Contractor Progress _____

Special Assignments _____

Extra Work	Authorized By	Approx. Price

Material Purchased	

Equipment Rented Today	Rented From	Rate

Supervisor's Signature _____

14 SEPT. 20___   DAILY LOG   DAY _____

CONTRACTOR _____ JOB NAME _____ JOB NO._____

Work Performed Today _____

_____

_____

_____

_____

_____

_____

_____

_____

_____

_____

_____

_____

Problems - Delays _____

_____

_____

_____

Sub-Contractor Progress _____

_____

_____

_____

Special Assignments _____

_____

_____

Weather	_____
Temp. AM _____ PM _____	
Safety Meeting _____	

Work Force	No.
Superintendent	_____
Clerk	_____
Bricklayers	_____
Carpenters	_____
Cement Masons	_____
Electricians	_____
Iron Workers	_____
Laborers	_____
Operating Eng.	_____
Plumbers	_____
Pipe Fitters	_____
Sheet Metal	_____
Truck Drivers	_____
Total	_____

Equipment	Hrs.

Extra Work	Authorized By	Approx. Price

Equipment Rented Today	Rented From	Rate

Material Purchased

Supervisor's Signature _____

DAY _____   DAILY LOG   20___ SEPT. 15

CONTRACTOR _____ JOB NAME _____ JOB NO _____

Work Performed Today _____

_____

_____

_____

_____

_____

_____

_____

_____

_____

_____

_____

_____

_____

Problems - Delays _____

_____

_____

_____

Sub-Contractor Progress _____

_____

_____

_____

Special Assignments _____

_____

_____

| Weather _____ |
| Temp. AM _____PM _____ |
| Safety Meeting _____ |

Work Force	No.
Superintendent	_____
Clerk	_____
Bricklayers	_____
Carpenters	_____
Cement Masons	_____
Electricians	_____
Iron Workers	_____
Laborers	_____
Operating Eng.	_____
Plumbers	_____
Pipe Fitters	_____
Sheet Metal	_____
Truck Drivers	_____
Total	_____

Equipment	Hrs.

Material Purchased

Extra Work	Authorized By	Approx. Price

Equipment Rented Today	Rented From	Rate

Supervisor's Signature _____

16 SEPT. 20___   DAILY LOG   DAY _____

CONTRACTOR _____ JOB NAME _____ JOB NO. _____

Work Performed Today _____

_____

_____

_____

_____

_____

_____

_____

_____

_____

_____

_____

_____

_____

Problems - Delays _____

_____

_____

_____

Sub-Contractor Progress _____

_____

_____

_____

Special Assignments _____

_____

_____

Weather	_____
Temp. AM _____ PM _____	
Safety Meeting _____	

Work Force	No.
Superintendent	_____
Clerk	_____
Bricklayers	_____
Carpenters	_____
Cement Masons	_____
Electricians	_____
Iron Workers	_____
Laborers	_____
Operating Eng.	_____
Plumbers	_____
Pipe Fitters	_____
Sheet Metal	_____
Truck Drivers	_____
Total	_____

Equipment	Hrs.

Extra Work	Authorized By	Approx. Price

Equipment Rented Today	Rented From	Rate

Material Purchased

Supervisor's Signature _____

DAY _____   DAILY LOG   20___ SEPT. 17

CONTRACTOR _____ JOB NAME _____ JOB NO _____

Work Performed Today _____

_____

_____

_____

_____

_____

_____

_____

_____

_____

_____

_____

_____

Problems - Delays _____

_____

_____

_____

Sub-Contractor Progress _____

_____

_____

_____

Special Assignments _____

_____

_____

Weather	
Temp. AM _____ PM _____	
Safety Meeting _____	

Work Force	No.
Superintendent	_____
Clerk	_____
Bricklayers	_____
Carpenters	_____
Cement Masons	_____
Electricians	_____
Iron Workers	_____
Laborers	_____
Operating Eng.	_____
Plumbers	_____
Pipe Fitters	_____
Sheet Metal	_____
Truck Drivers	_____
Total	_____

Equipment	Hrs.

Extra Work	Authorized By	Approx. Price

Equipment Rented Today	Rented From	Rate

Material Purchased

Supervisor's Signature _____

18 SEPT. 20___   DAILY LOG   DAY _____

CONTRACTOR _____ JOB NAME _____ JOB NO._____

Work Performed Today _____

_____

_____

_____

_____

_____

_____

_____

_____

_____

_____

_____

_____

_____

_____

Problems - Delays _____

_____

_____

_____

Sub-Contractor Progress _____

_____

_____

_____

Special Assignments _____

_____

_____

| Weather _____ |
| Temp. AM _____PM _____ |
| Safety Meeting _____ |

Work Force	No.
Superintendent	_____
Clerk	_____
Bricklayers	_____
Carpenters	_____
Cement Masons	_____
Electricians	_____
Iron Workers	_____
Laborers	_____
Operating Eng.	_____
Plumbers	_____
Pipe Fitters	_____
Sheet Metal	_____
Truck Drivers	_____
Total	_____

Equipment	Hrs.

Extra Work	Authorized By	Approx. Price

Equipment Rented Today	Rented From	Rate

Material Purchased

Supervisor's Signature _____

DAY _____   DAILY LOG   20____ SEPT. 19

CONTRACTOR _____ JOB NAME _____ JOB NO _____

Work Performed Today _____

_____

_____

_____

_____

_____

_____

_____

_____

_____

_____

_____

_____

_____

_____

Problems - Delays _____

_____

_____

_____

Sub-Contractor Progress _____

_____

_____

_____

Special Assignments _____

_____

_____

Extra Work	Authorized By	Approx. Price

Equipment Rented Today	Rented From	Rate

Supervisor's Signature _____

Weather _____

Temp. AM _____ PM _____

Safety Meeting _____

Work Force	No.
Superintendent	_____
Clerk	_____
Bricklayers	_____
Carpenters	_____
Cement Masons	_____
Electricians	_____
Iron Workers	_____
Laborers	_____
Operating Eng.	_____
Plumbers	_____
Pipe Fitters	_____
Sheet Metal	_____
Truck Drivers	_____
Total	_____

Equipment	Hrs.

Material Purchased

20 SEPT. 20___   DAILY LOG   DAY _____

CONTRACTOR _____ JOB NAME _____ JOB NO._____

Work Performed Today _____

_____

_____

_____

_____

_____

_____

_____

_____

_____

_____

_____

_____

_____

Problems - Delays _____

_____

_____

_____

Sub-Contractor Progress _____

_____

_____

_____

Special Assignments _____

_____

_____

Extra Work	Authorized By	Approx. Price

Equipment Rented Today	Rented From	Rate

Supervisor's Signature _____

Weather _____

Temp. AM _____ PM _____

Safety Meeting _____

Work Force	No.
Superintendent	_____
Clerk	_____
Bricklayers	_____
Carpenters	_____
Cement Masons	_____
Electricians	_____
Iron Workers	_____
Laborers	_____
Operating Eng.	_____
Plumbers	_____
Pipe Fitters	_____
Sheet Metal	_____
Truck Drivers	_____
Total	_____

Equipment	Hrs.

Material Purchased

DAY _____   DAILY LOG   20___ SEPT. 21

CONTRACTOR _____ JOB NAME _____ JOB NO _____

Work Performed Today _____

_____

_____

_____

_____

_____

_____

_____

_____

_____

_____

_____

_____

Problems - Delays _____

_____

_____

_____

Sub-Contractor Progress _____

_____

_____

_____

Special Assignments _____

_____

_____

_____

Extra Work	Authorized By	Approx. Price

Equipment Rented Today	Rented From	Rate

Supervisor's Signature _____

Weather _____

Temp. AM _____ PM _____

Safety Meeting _____

Work Force	No.
Superintendent	_____
Clerk	_____
Bricklayers	_____
Carpenters	_____
Cement Masons	_____
Electricians	_____
Iron Workers	_____
Laborers	_____
Operating Eng.	_____
Plumbers	_____
Pipe Fitters	_____
Sheet Metal	_____
Truck Drivers	_____
Total	_____

Equipment	Hrs.

Material Purchased

22 SEPT. 20___   DAILY LOG   DAY _____

CONTRACTOR _____ JOB NAME _____ JOB NO._____

Work Performed Today _____	Weather _____
	Temp. AM _____PM _____
	Safety Meeting _____

Work Force	No.
Superintendent	_____
Clerk	_____
Bricklayers	_____
Carpenters	_____
Cement Masons	_____
Electricians	_____
Iron Workers	_____
Laborers	_____
Operating Eng.	_____
Plumbers	_____
Pipe Fitters	_____
Sheet Metal	_____
Truck Drivers	_____
Total	_____

Problems - Delays _____

Sub-Contractor Progress _____

Equipment	Hrs.

Special Assignments _____

Extra Work	Authorized By	Approx. Price

Equipment Rented Today	Rented From	Rate

Material Purchased

Supervisor's Signature _____

DAY _____   DAILY LOG   20___ SEPT. 23

CONTRACTOR _____ JOB NAME _____ JOB NO _____

Work Performed Today _____	Weather _____
	Temp. AM _____ PM _____
	Safety Meeting _____

Work Force	**No.**
Superintendent	_____
Clerk	_____
Bricklayers	_____
Carpenters	_____
Cement Masons	_____
Electricians	_____
Iron Workers	_____
Laborers	_____
Operating Eng.	_____
Plumbers	_____
Pipe Fitters	_____
Sheet Metal	_____
Truck Drivers	_____
Total	_____

Problems - Delays _____

Equipment	Hrs.

Sub-Contractor Progress _____

Special Assignments _____

Extra Work	Authorized By	Approx. Price

Material Purchased	

Equipment Rented Today	Rented From	Rate

Supervisor's Signature _____

24 SEPT. 20___   DAILY LOG   DAY _____

CONTRACTOR _____ JOB NAME _____ JOB NO._____

Work Performed Today _____

_____

_____

_____

_____

_____

_____

_____

_____

_____

_____

_____

_____

_____

Problems - Delays _____

_____

_____

_____

Sub-Contractor Progress _____

_____

_____

_____

Special Assignments _____

_____

_____

_____

| Weather | _____ |
| Temp. AM _____PM _____ | |

| Safety Meeting _____ | |

Work Force	No.
Superintendent	_____
Clerk	_____
Bricklayers	_____
Carpenters	_____
Cement Masons	_____
Electricians	_____
Iron Workers	_____
Laborers	_____
Operating Eng.	_____
Plumbers	_____
Pipe Fitters	_____
Sheet Metal	_____
Truck Drivers	_____
Total	_____

Equipment	Hrs.

Material Purchased	

Extra Work	Authorized By	Approx. Price

Equipment Rented Today	Rented From	Rate

Supervisor's Signature _____

DAY _____   DAILY LOG   20___ SEPT. 25

CONTRACTOR _____ JOB NAME _____ JOB NO _____

Work Performed Today _____

_____

_____

_____

_____

_____

_____

_____

_____

_____

_____

_____

_____

Problems - Delays _____

_____

_____

_____

Sub-Contractor Progress _____

_____

_____

_____

Special Assignments _____

_____

_____

Weather	
Temp. AM _____ PM _____	
Safety Meeting _____	

Work Force	No.
Superintendent	_____
Clerk	_____
Bricklayers	_____
Carpenters	_____
Cement Masons	_____
Electricians	_____
Iron Workers	_____
Laborers	_____
Operating Eng.	_____
Plumbers	_____
Pipe Fitters	_____
Sheet Metal	_____
Truck Drivers	_____
Total	_____

Equipment	Hrs.

Extra Work	Authorized By	Approx. Price

Equipment Rented Today	Rented From	Rate

Material Purchased

Supervisor's Signature _____

26 SEPT. 20___   DAILY LOG   DAY _____

CONTRACTOR _____ JOB NAME _____ JOB NO._____

Work Performed Today _____	Weather _____
_____	Temp. AM _____PM _____
_____	Safety Meeting _____

Work Force	No.
Superintendent	_____
Clerk	_____
Bricklayers	_____
Carpenters	_____
Cement Masons	_____
Electricians	_____
Iron Workers	_____
Laborers	_____
Operating Eng.	_____
Plumbers	_____
Pipe Fitters	_____
Sheet Metal	_____
Truck Drivers	_____
Total	_____

Problems - Delays _____

Sub-Contractor Progress _____

Special Assignments _____

Equipment	Hrs.

Extra Work	Authorized By	Approx. Price

Equipment Rented Today	Rented From	Rate

Material Purchased

Supervisor's Signature _____

DAY _____   DAILY LOG   20____ SEPT. 27

CONTRACTOR _____ JOB NAME _____ JOB NO _____

Work Performed Today _____

_____

_____

_____

_____

_____

_____

_____

_____

_____

_____

_____

_____

_____

Problems - Delays _____

_____

_____

_____

_____

Sub-Contractor Progress _____

_____

_____

_____

Special Assignments _____

_____

_____

| Weather _____ |
| Temp. AM _____ PM _____ |
| Safety Meeting _____ |

Work Force	No.
Superintendent	_____
Clerk	_____
Bricklayers	_____
Carpenters	_____
Cement Masons	_____
Electricians	_____
Iron Workers	_____
Laborers	_____
Operating Eng.	_____
Plumbers	
Pipe Fitters	_____
Sheet Metal	
Truck Drivers	_____
Total	_____

Equipment	Hrs.

Material Purchased

Extra Work	Authorized By	Approx. Price

Equipment Rented Today	Rented From	Rate

Supervisor's Signature _____

28 SEPT. 20___   DAILY LOG   DAY _____

CONTRACTOR _____ JOB NAME _____ JOB NO._____

Work Performed Today _____	Weather _____
_____	Temp. AM _____ PM _____
_____	Safety Meeting _____
_____	**Work Force** **No.**
_____	Superintendent _____
_____	Clerk _____
_____	Bricklayers _____
_____	Carpenters _____
_____	Cement Masons _____
_____	Electricians _____
_____	Iron Workers _____
_____	Laborers _____
_____	Operating Eng. _____
_____	Plumbers _____
_____	Pipe Fitters _____
_____	Sheet Metal _____
_____	Truck Drivers _____

Problems - Delays _____

_____

_____

_____

Total _____

Sub-Contractor Progress _____

Equipment	Hrs.

Special Assignments _____

_____

_____

Material Purchased

Extra Work	Authorized By	Approx. Price

Equipment Rented Today	Rented From	Rate

Supervisor's Signature _____

DAY _____   DAILY LOG   20 ___ SEPT. 29

CONTRACTOR _____ JOB NAME _____ JOB NO _____

Work Performed Today _____	Weather _____

Work Performed Today _____

_____

_____

_____

_____

_____

_____

_____

_____

_____

_____

_____

_____

Problems - Delays _____

_____

_____

_____

Sub-Contractor Progress _____

_____

_____

_____

Special Assignments _____

_____

_____

Weather _____

Temp. AM _____ PM _____

Safety Meeting _____

Work Force	No.
Superintendent	_____
Clerk	_____
Bricklayers	_____
Carpenters	_____
Cement Masons	_____
Electricians	_____
Iron Workers	_____
Laborers	_____
Operating Eng.	_____
Plumbers	_____
Pipe Fitters	_____
Sheet Metal	_____
Truck Drivers	_____
Total	_____

Equipment	Hrs.

Extra Work	Authorized By	Approx. Price

Equipment Rented Today	Rented From	Rate

Material Purchased

Supervisor's Signature _____

30 SEPT. 20___   DAILY LOG   DAY _____

CONTRACTOR _____ JOB NAME _____ JOB NO. _____

Work Performed Today _____

_____

_____

_____

_____

_____

_____

_____

_____

_____

_____

_____

_____

Problems - Delays _____

_____

_____

_____

Sub-Contractor Progress _____

_____

_____

Special Assignments _____

_____

_____

Extra Work	Authorized By	Approx. Price

Equipment Rented Today	Rented From	Rate

Supervisor's Signature _____

Weather _____

Temp. AM _____ PM _____

Safety Meeting _____

Work Force	No.
Superintendent	_____
Clerk	_____
Bricklayers	_____
Carpenters	_____
Cement Masons	_____
Electricians	_____
Iron Workers	_____
Laborers	_____
Operating Eng.	_____
Plumbers	_____
Pipe Fitters	_____
Sheet Metal	_____
Truck Drivers	_____
Total	_____

Equipment	Hrs.

Material Purchased

DAY _____   DAILY LOG   20___ OCT. 1

CONTRACTOR _____ JOB NAME _____ JOB NO _____

Work Performed Today _____

_____

_____

_____

_____

_____

_____

_____

_____

_____

_____

_____

_____

_____

Problems - Delays _____

_____

_____

_____

Sub-Contractor Progress _____

_____

_____

_____

Special Assignments _____

_____

_____

Weather	
Temp. AM _____ PM _____	
Safety Meeting _____	

Work Force	No.
Superintendent	_____
Clerk	_____
Bricklayers	_____
Carpenters	_____
Cement Masons	_____
Electricians	_____
Iron Workers	_____
Laborers	_____
Operating Eng.	_____
Plumbers	_____
Pipe Fitters	_____
Sheet Metal	_____
Truck Drivers	_____
Total	_____

Equipment	Hrs.

Material Purchased	

Extra Work	Authorized By	Approx. Price

Equipment Rented Today	Rented From	Rate

Supervisor's Signature _____

2 OCT. 20___   DAILY LOG   DAY _____

CONTRACTOR _____ JOB NAME _____ JOB NO._____

Work Performed Today _____

_____

_____

_____

_____

_____

_____

_____

_____

_____

_____

_____

_____

_____

Problems - Delays _____

_____

_____

_____

Sub-Contractor Progress _____

_____

_____

_____

Special Assignments _____

_____

_____

| Weather _____ |
| Temp. AM _____PM ____ |
| Safety Meeting _____ |

Work Force	No.
Superintendent	_____
Clerk	_____
Bricklayers	_____
Carpenters	_____
Cement Masons	_____
Electricians	_____
Iron Workers	_____
Laborers	_____
Operating Eng.	_____
Plumbers	_____
Pipe Fitters	_____
Sheet Metal	_____
Truck Drivers	_____
Total	_____

Equipment	Hrs.

Extra Work	Authorized By	Approx. Price

Equipment Rented Today	Rented From	Rate

Material Purchased

Supervisor's Signature _____

DAY _____   DAILY LOG   20___ OCT. 3

CONTRACTOR _____ JOB NAME _____ JOB NO _____

Work Performed Today _____

_____

_____

_____

_____

_____

_____

_____

_____

_____

_____

_____

_____

Problems - Delays _____

_____

_____

_____

Sub-Contractor Progress _____

_____

_____

_____

Special Assignments _____

_____

_____

Weather		
Temp. AM _____ PM _____		
Safety Meeting _____		

Work Force	No.
Superintendent	_____
Clerk	_____
Bricklayers	_____
Carpenters	_____
Cement Masons	_____
Electricians	_____
Iron Workers	_____
Laborers	_____
Operating Eng.	_____
Plumbers	_____
Pipe Fitters	_____
Sheet Metal	_____
Truck Drivers	_____
Total	_____

Equipment	Hrs.

Extra Work	Authorized By	Approx. Price

Equipment Rented Today	Rented From	Rate

Material Purchased

Supervisor's Signature _____

4 OCT. 20___   DAILY LOG   DAY _____

CONTRACTOR _____ JOB NAME _____ JOB NO._____

Work Performed Today _____

_____

_____

_____

_____

_____

_____

_____

_____

_____

_____

_____

_____

Problems - Delays _____

_____

_____

_____

Sub-Contractor Progress _____

_____

_____

_____

Special Assignments _____

_____

_____

Weather _____

Temp. AM _____ PM _____

Safety Meeting _____

Work Force	No.
Superintendent	_____
Clerk	_____
Bricklayers	_____
Carpenters	_____
Cement Masons	_____
Electricians	_____
Iron Workers	_____
Laborers	_____
Operating Eng.	_____
Plumbers	_____
Pipe Fitters	_____
Sheet Metal	_____
Truck Drivers	_____
Total	_____

Equipment	Hrs.

Extra Work	Authorized By	Approx. Price

Equipment Rented Today	Rented From	Rate

Material Purchased

Supervisor's Signature _____

DAY _____   DAILY LOG   20___ OCT. 5

CONTRACTOR _____ JOB NAME _____ JOB NO _____

Work Performed Today _____	Weather _____
	Temp. AM _____ PM _____
	Safety Meeting _____

Work Force	No.
Superintendent	____
Clerk	____
Bricklayers	____
Carpenters	____
Cement Masons	____
Electricians	____
Iron Workers	____
Laborers	____
Operating Eng.	____
Plumbers	____
Pipe Fitters	____
Sheet Metal	____
Truck Drivers	____
Total	____

Problems - Delays _____

Equipment	Hrs.

Sub-Contractor Progress _____

Special Assignments _____

Material Purchased	

Extra Work	Authorized By	Approx. Price

Equipment Rented Today	Rented From	Rate

Supervisor's Signature _____

6 OCT. 20____   DAILY LOG   DAY _____

CONTRACTOR _____ JOB NAME _____ JOB NO. _____

Work Performed Today _____

_____

_____

_____

_____

_____

_____

_____

_____

_____

_____

_____

_____

_____

Problems - Delays _____

_____

_____

_____

Sub-Contractor Progress _____

_____

_____

_____

Special Assignments _____

_____

_____

Weather	_____
Temp. AM _____ PM _____	
Safety Meeting _____	

Work Force	No.
Superintendent	_____
Clerk	_____
Bricklayers	_____
Carpenters	_____
Cement Masons	_____
Electricians	_____
Iron Workers	_____
Laborers	_____
Operating Eng.	_____
Plumbers	_____
Pipe Fitters	_____
Sheet Metal	_____
Truck Drivers	_____
Total	_____

Equipment	Hrs.

Extra Work	Authorized By	Approx. Price

Equipment Rented Today	Rented From	Rate

Material Purchased

Supervisor's Signature _____

DAY _____   DAILY LOG   20___ OCT. 7

CONTRACTOR _____ JOB NAME _____ JOB NO _____

Work Performed Today _____	Weather _____
	Temp. AM _____PM _____
	Safety Meeting _____

Work Force	No.
Superintendent	_____
Clerk	_____
Bricklayers	_____
Carpenters	_____
Cement Masons	_____
Electricians	_____
Iron Workers	_____
Laborers	_____
Operating Eng.	_____
Plumbers	_____
Pipe Fitters	_____
Sheet Metal	_____
Truck Drivers	_____
Total	_____

Problems - Delays _____

Sub-Contractor Progress _____

Equipment	Hrs.

Special Assignments _____

Extra Work	Authorized By	Approx. Price

Equipment Rented Today	Rented From	Rate

Material Purchased

Supervisor's Signature _____

8 OCT. 20___   DAILY LOG   DAY _____

CONTRACTOR _____ JOB NAME _____ JOB NO._____

Work Performed Today _____		Weather _____
		Temp. AM _____PM _____
		Safety Meeting _____

Work Force	No.
Superintendent	_____
Clerk	_____
Bricklayers	_____
Carpenters	_____
Cement Masons	_____
Electricians	_____
Iron Workers	_____
Laborers	_____
Operating Eng.	_____
Plumbers	_____
Pipe Fitters	_____
Sheet Metal	_____
Truck Drivers	_____
Total	_____

Problems - Delays _____

Equipment	Hrs.

Sub-Contractor Progress _____

Special Assignments _____

Material Purchased	

Extra Work	Authorized By	Approx. Price

Equipment Rented Today	Rented From	Rate

Supervisor's Signature _____

DAY _____   DAILY LOG   20___ OCT. 9

CONTRACTOR _____ JOB NAME _____ JOB NO _____

Work Performed Today _____	Weather _____
	Temp. AM _____ PM _____
	Safety Meeting _____

Work Force	No.
Superintendent	_____
Clerk	_____
Bricklayers	_____
Carpenters	_____
Cement Masons	_____
Electricians	_____
Iron Workers	_____
Laborers	_____
Operating Eng.	_____
Plumbers	_____
Pipe Fitters	_____
Sheet Metal	_____
Truck Drivers	_____
Total	_____

Problems - Delays _____

Equipment	Hrs.

Sub-Contractor Progress _____

Special Assignments _____

Extra Work	Authorized By	Approx. Price

Material Purchased

Equipment Rented Today	Rented From	Rate

Supervisor's Signature _____

10 OCT. 20___   DAILY LOG   DAY _____

CONTRACTOR _____ JOB NAME _____ JOB NO._____

Work Performed Today _____

_____

_____

_____

_____

_____

_____

_____

_____

_____

_____

_____

_____

_____

_____

_____

Problems - Delays _____

_____

_____

_____

Sub-Contractor Progress _____

_____

_____

_____

Special Assignments _____

_____

_____

Weather	_____
Temp. AM _____PM _____	
Safety Meeting _____	

Work Force	No.
Superintendent	_____
Clerk	_____
Bricklayers	_____
Carpenters	_____
Cement Masons	_____
Electricians	_____
Iron Workers	_____
Laborers	_____
Operating Eng.	_____
Plumbers	_____
Pipe Fitters	_____
Sheet Metal	_____
Truck Drivers	_____
Total	_____

Equipment	Hrs.

Extra Work	Authorized By	Approx. Price

Equipment Rented Today	Rented From	Rate

Material Purchased

Supervisor's Signature _____

DAY _____   DAILY LOG   20___ OCT. 11

CONTRACTOR _____ JOB NAME _____ JOB NO _____

Work Performed Today _____	Weather _____
_____	Temp. AM _____ PM _____
_____	Safety Meeting _____

	Work Force	No.
	Superintendent	_____
	Clerk	_____
	Bricklayers	_____
	Carpenters	_____
	Cement Masons	_____
	Electricians	_____
	Iron Workers	_____
	Laborers	_____
	Operating Eng.	_____
	Plumbers	_____
	Pipe Fitters	_____
	Sheet Metal	_____
	Truck Drivers	_____

Problems - Delays _____

Total   _____

Equipment	Hrs.

Sub-Contractor Progress _____

Special Assignments _____

Extra Work	Authorized By	Approx. Price

Material Purchased

Equipment Rented Today	Rented From	Rate

Supervisor's Signature _____

12 OCT. 20___   DAILY LOG   DAY _____

CONTRACTOR _____ JOB NAME _____ JOB NO._____

Work Performed Today _____

_____

_____

_____

_____

_____

_____

_____

_____

_____

_____

_____

_____

_____

Problems - Delays _____

_____

_____

_____

Sub-Contractor Progress _____

_____

_____

_____

Special Assignments _____

_____

_____

Extra Work	Authorized By	Approx. Price

Equipment Rented Today	Rented From	Rate

Supervisor's Signature _____

Weather _____

Temp. AM _____PM _____

Safety Meeting _____

Work Force	No.
Superintendent	_____
Clerk	_____
Bricklayers	_____
Carpenters	_____
Cement Masons	_____
Electricians	_____
Iron Workers	_____
Laborers	_____
Operating Eng.	_____
Plumbers	_____
Pipe Fitters	_____
Sheet Metal	_____
Truck Drivers	_____
Total	_____

Equipment	Hrs.

Material Purchased

DAY _____   DAILY LOG   20___ OCT. 13

CONTRACTOR _____ JOB NAME _____ JOB NO _____

Work Performed Today _____

_____

_____

_____

_____

_____

_____

_____

_____

_____

_____

_____

_____

_____

Problems - Delays _____

_____

_____

_____

Sub-Contractor Progress _____

_____

_____

_____

Special Assignments _____

_____

_____

Weather	_____
Temp. AM _____ PM _____	
Safety Meeting _____	

Work Force	No.
Superintendent	_____
Clerk	_____
Bricklayers	_____
Carpenters	_____
Cement Masons	_____
Electricians	_____
Iron Workers	_____
Laborers	_____
Operating Eng.	_____
Plumbers	_____
Pipe Fitters	_____
Sheet Metal	_____
Truck Drivers	_____
Total	_____

Equipment	Hrs.

Extra Work	Authorized By	Approx. Price

Equipment Rented Today	Rented From	Rate

Material Purchased

Supervisor's Signature _____

14 OCT. 20___   DAILY LOG   DAY _____

CONTRACTOR _____ JOB NAME _____ JOB NO._____

Work Performed Today _____

_____

_____

_____

_____

_____

_____

_____

_____

_____

_____

_____

_____

_____

Problems - Delays _____

_____

_____

_____

Sub-Contractor Progress _____

_____

_____

_____

Special Assignments _____

_____

_____

Weather		
Temp. AM _____PM _____		
Safety Meeting _____		

Work Force	No.
Superintendent	_____
Clerk	_____
Bricklayers	_____
Carpenters	_____
Cement Masons	_____
Electricians	_____
Iron Workers	_____
Laborers	_____
Operating Eng.	_____
Plumbers	_____
Pipe Fitters	_____
Sheet Metal	_____
Truck Drivers	_____
Total	_____

Equipment	Hrs.

Material Purchased

Extra Work	Authorized By	Approx. Price

Equipment Rented Today	Rented From	Rate

Supervisor's Signature _____

DAY _____   DAILY LOG   20___ OCT. 15

CONTRACTOR _____ JOB NAME _____ JOB NO _____

Work Performed Today _____

_____

_____

_____

_____

_____

_____

_____

_____

_____

_____

_____

_____

Problems - Delays _____

_____

_____

_____

Sub-Contractor Progress _____

_____

_____

_____

Special Assignments _____

_____

_____

Weather	
Temp. AM _____ PM _____	
Safety Meeting _____	

Work Force	No.
Superintendent	_____
Clerk	_____
Bricklayers	_____
Carpenters	_____
Cement Masons	_____
Electricians	_____
Iron Workers	_____
Laborers	_____
Operating Eng.	_____
Plumbers	_____
Pipe Fitters	_____
Sheet Metal	_____
Truck Drivers	_____
Total	_____

Equipment	Hrs.

Material Purchased

Extra Work	Authorized By	Approx. Price

Equipment Rented Today	Rented From	Rate

Supervisor's Signature _____

16 OCT. 20____   DAILY LOG   DAY _____

CONTRACTOR _____ JOB NAME _____ JOB NO._____

Work Performed Today _____

_____

_____

_____

_____

_____

_____

_____

_____

_____

_____

_____

_____

_____

Problems - Delays _____

_____

_____

_____

Sub-Contractor Progress _____

_____

_____

_____

Special Assignments _____

_____

_____

Weather	_____
Temp. AM _____ PM _____	
Safety Meeting _____	

Work Force	No.
Superintendent	_____
Clerk	_____
Bricklayers	_____
Carpenters	_____
Cement Masons	_____
Electricians	_____
Iron Workers	_____
Laborers	_____
Operating Eng.	_____
Plumbers	_____
Pipe Fitters	_____
Sheet Metal	_____
Truck Drivers	_____
Total	_____

Equipment	Hrs.

Extra Work	Authorized By	Approx. Price

Equipment Rented Today	Rented From	Rate

Material Purchased

Supervisor's Signature _____

DAY _____   DAILY LOG   20___ OCT. 17

CONTRACTOR _____ JOB NAME _____ JOB NO _____

Work Performed Today _____

_____

_____

_____

_____

_____

_____

_____

_____

_____

_____

_____

_____

Problems - Delays _____

_____

_____

_____

Sub-Contractor Progress _____

_____

_____

Special Assignments _____

_____

_____

| Weather _____ |
| Temp. AM _____ PM _____ |
| Safety Meeting _____ |

Work Force	No.
Superintendent	___
Clerk	___
Bricklayers	___
Carpenters	___
Cement Masons	___
Electricians	___
Iron Workers	___
Laborers	___
Operating Eng.	___
Plumbers	___
Pipe Fitters	___
Sheet Metal	___
Truck Drivers	___
Total	___

Equipment	Hrs.

Extra Work	Authorized By	Approx. Price

Equipment Rented Today	Rented From	Rate

Material Purchased

Supervisor's Signature _____

18 OCT. 20____   DAILY LOG   DAY _____

CONTRACTOR _____ JOB NAME _____ JOB NO. _____

Work Performed Today _____

_____

_____

_____

_____

_____

_____

_____

_____

_____

_____

_____

_____

Problems - Delays _____

_____

_____

_____

Sub-Contractor Progress _____

_____

_____

_____

Special Assignments _____

_____

_____

Weather	_____
Temp. AM _____ PM _____	
Safety Meeting _____	

Work Force	No.
Superintendent	_____
Clerk	_____
Bricklayers	_____
Carpenters	_____
Cement Masons	_____
Electricians	_____
Iron Workers	_____
Laborers	_____
Operating Eng.	_____
Plumbers	_____
Pipe Fitters	_____
Sheet Metal	_____
Truck Drivers	_____
Total	_____

Equipment	Hrs.

Material Purchased	

Extra Work	Authorized By	Approx. Price

Equipment Rented Today	Rented From	Rate

Supervisor's Signature _____

DAY _____   DAILY LOG   20___ OCT. 19

CONTRACTOR _____ JOB NAME _____ JOB NO _____

Work Performed Today _____

_____

_____

_____

_____

_____

_____

_____

_____

_____

_____

_____

_____

Problems - Delays _____

_____

_____

_____

Sub-Contractor Progress _____

_____

_____

_____

Special Assignments _____

_____

_____

_____

Weather	_____
Temp. AM _____ PM _____	
Safety Meeting _____	

Work Force	No.
Superintendent	_____
Clerk	_____
Bricklayers	_____
Carpenters	_____
Cement Masons	_____
Electricians	_____
Iron Workers	_____
Laborers	_____
Operating Eng.	_____
Plumbers	_____
Pipe Fitters	_____
Sheet Metal	_____
Truck Drivers	_____
Total	_____

Equipment	Hrs.

Material Purchased	

Extra Work	Authorized By	Approx. Price

Equipment Rented Today	Rented From	Rate

Supervisor's Signature _____

20 OCT. 20____   DAILY LOG   DAY _____

CONTRACTOR _____ JOB NAME _____ JOB NO._____

Work Performed Today _____	Weather _____
	Temp. AM _____PM _____
	Safety Meeting _____

Work Force	No.
Superintendent	_____
Clerk	_____
Bricklayers	_____
Carpenters	_____
Cement Masons	_____
Electricians	_____
Iron Workers	_____
Laborers	_____
Operating Eng.	_____
Plumbers	_____
Pipe Fitters	_____
Sheet Metal	_____
Truck Drivers	_____
Total	_____

Problems - Delays _____

Equipment	Hrs.

Sub-Contractor Progress _____

Special Assignments _____

Extra Work	Authorized By	Approx. Price

Equipment Rented Today	Rented From	Rate

Material Purchased

Supervisor's Signature _____

DAY _____   DAILY LOG   20___ OCT. 21

CONTRACTOR _____ JOB NAME _____ JOB NO _____

Work Performed Today _____

_____

_____

_____

_____

_____

_____

_____

_____

_____

_____

_____

Problems - Delays _____

_____

_____

_____

Sub-Contractor Progress _____

_____

_____

_____

Special Assignments _____

_____

_____

Weather	
Temp. AM _____ PM _____	
Safety Meeting _____	

Work Force	No.
Superintendent	_____
Clerk	_____
Bricklayers	_____
Carpenters	_____
Cement Masons	_____
Electricians	_____
Iron Workers	_____
Laborers	_____
Operating Eng.	_____
Plumbers	_____
Pipe Fitters	_____
Sheet Metal	_____
Truck Drivers	_____
Total	_____

Equipment	Hrs.

Extra Work	Authorized By	Approx. Price

Equipment Rented Today	Rented From	Rate

Material Purchased

Supervisor's Signature _____

22 OCT. 20___   DAILY LOG   DAY _____

CONTRACTOR _____ JOB NAME _____ JOB NO._____

Work Performed Today _____

_____

_____

_____

_____

_____

_____

_____

_____

_____

_____

_____

_____

_____

_____

Problems - Delays _____

_____

_____

_____

Sub-Contractor Progress _____

_____

_____

_____

Special Assignments _____

_____

Weather _____
Temp. AM _____PM _____
Safety Meeting _____

Work Force	No.
Superintendent	_____
Clerk	_____
Bricklayers	_____
Carpenters	_____
Cement Masons	_____
Electricians	_____
Iron Workers	_____
Laborers	_____
Operating Eng.	_____
Plumbers	_____
Pipe Fitters	_____
Sheet Metal	_____
Truck Drivers	_____
Total	_____

Equipment	Hrs.

Material Purchased	

Extra Work	Authorized By	Approx. Price

Equipment Rented Today	Rented From	Rate

Supervisor's Signature _____

DAY _____ DAILY LOG 20___ OCT. 23

CONTRACTOR _____ JOB NAME _____ JOB NO _____

| Work Performed Today _____ | Weather _____ |

Temp. AM _____ PM _____

Safety Meeting _____

Work Force	No.
Superintendent	_____
Clerk	_____
Bricklayers	_____
Carpenters	_____
Cement Masons	_____
Electricians	_____
Iron Workers	_____
Laborers	_____
Operating Eng.	_____
Plumbers	_____
Pipe Fitters	_____
Sheet Metal	_____
Truck Drivers	_____
Total	_____

Work Performed Today section (lines for writing)

Problems - Delays _____

Equipment	Hrs.

Sub-Contractor Progress _____

Special Assignments _____

Material Purchased

Extra Work	Authorized By	Approx. Price

Equipment Rented Today	Rented From	Rate

Supervisor's Signature _____

24 OCT. 20___   DAILY LOG   DAY _____

CONTRACTOR _____ JOB NAME _____ JOB NO._____

Work Performed Today _____

_____

_____

_____

_____

_____

_____

_____

_____

_____

_____

_____

_____

_____

_____

Problems - Delays _____

_____

_____

_____

Sub-Contractor Progress _____

_____

_____

_____

Special Assignments _____

_____

_____

Weather	_____
Temp. AM _____ PM _____	
Safety Meeting _____	

Work Force	No.
Superintendent	_____
Clerk	_____
Bricklayers	_____
Carpenters	_____
Cement Masons	_____
Electricians	_____
Iron Workers	_____
Laborers	_____
Operating Eng.	_____
Plumbers	_____
Pipe Fitters	_____
Sheet Metal	_____
Truck Drivers	_____
Total	_____

Equipment	Hrs.

Extra Work	Authorized By	Approx. Price

Equipment Rented Today	Rented From	Rate

Material Purchased

Supervisor's Signature _____

DAY _____   DAILY LOG   20___ OCT. 25

CONTRACTOR _____ JOB NAME _____ JOB NO _____

Work Performed Today _____

_____

_____

_____

_____

_____

_____

_____

_____

_____

_____

_____

_____

_____

Problems - Delays _____

_____

_____

_____

Sub-Contractor Progress _____

_____

_____

_____

Special Assignments _____

_____

_____

Extra Work	Authorized By	Approx. Price

Equipment Rented Today	Rented From	Rate

Supervisor's Signature _____

Weather _____

Temp. AM _____ PM _____

Safety Meeting _____

Work Force	No.
Superintendent	_____
Clerk	_____
Bricklayers	_____
Carpenters	_____
Cement Masons	_____
Electricians	_____
Iron Workers	_____
Laborers	_____
Operating Eng.	_____
Plumbers	_____
Pipe Fitters	_____
Sheet Metal	_____
Truck Drivers	_____
Total	_____

Equipment	Hrs.

Material Purchased

26 OCT. 20___   DAILY LOG   DAY _____

CONTRACTOR _____ JOB NAME _____ JOB NO._____

Work Performed Today _____

_____

_____

_____

_____

_____

_____

_____

_____

_____

_____

_____

_____

_____

Problems - Delays _____

_____

_____

_____

Sub-Contractor Progress _____

_____

_____

_____

Special Assignments _____

_____

_____

| Weather _____ |
| Temp. AM _____PM _____ |
| Safety Meeting _____ |

Work Force	No.
Superintendent	_____
Clerk	_____
Bricklayers	_____
Carpenters	_____
Cement Masons	_____
Electricians	_____
Iron Workers	_____
Laborers	_____
Operating Eng.	_____
Plumbers	_____
Pipe Fitters	_____
Sheet Metal	_____
Truck Drivers	_____
Total	_____

Equipment	Hrs.

Material Purchased

Extra Work	Authorized By	Approx. Price

Equipment Rented Today	Rented From	Rate

Supervisor's Signature _____

DAY _____   DAILY LOG   20___   OCT. 27

CONTRACTOR _____ JOB NAME _____ JOB NO _____

Work Performed Today _____	Weather _____
_____	Temp. AM _____PM _____
_____	Safety Meeting _____

Work Force	**No.**
Superintendent	_____
Clerk	_____
Bricklayers	_____
Carpenters	_____
Cement Masons	_____
Electricians	_____
Iron Workers	_____
Laborers	_____
Operating Eng.	_____
Plumbers	
Pipe Fitters	
Sheet Metal	
Truck Drivers	_____
Total	_____

Problems - Delays _____

Sub-Contractor Progress _____

Equipment	Hrs.

Special Assignments _____

Extra Work	Authorized By	Approx. Price

Equipment Rented Today	Rented From	Rate

Material Purchased

Supervisor's Signature _____

28 OCT. 20___   DAILY LOG   DAY _____

CONTRACTOR _____ JOB NAME _____ JOB NO._____

Work Performed Today _____	Weather_____
	Temp. AM _____PM _____
_____	Safety Meeting _____

Work Force	No.
Superintendent	_____
Clerk	_____
Bricklayers	_____
Carpenters	_____
Cement Masons	_____
Electricians	_____
Iron Workers	_____
Laborers	_____
Operating Eng.	_____
Plumbers	_____
Pipe Fitters	_____
Sheet Metal	_____
Truck Drivers	_____
Total	_____

Problems - Delays _____

Sub-Contractor Progress _____

Equipment	Hrs.

Special Assignments _____

Extra Work	Authorized By	Approx. Price

Equipment Rented Today	Rented From	Rate

Material Purchased

Supervisor's Signature _____

DAY _____   DAILY LOG   20___ OCT. 29

CONTRACTOR _____ JOB NAME _____ JOB NO _____

Work Performed Today _____

_____

_____

_____

_____

_____

_____

_____

_____

_____

_____

_____

Problems - Delays _____

_____

_____

_____

Sub-Contractor Progress _____

_____

_____

_____

Special Assignments _____

_____

_____

Extra Work	Authorized By	Approx. Price

Equipment Rented Today	Rented From	Rate

Supervisor's Signature _____

Weather _____

Temp. AM _____ PM _____

Safety Meeting _____

Work Force	No.
Superintendent	
Clerk	
Bricklayers	
Carpenters	
Cement Masons	
Electricians	
Iron Workers	
Laborers	
Operating Eng.	
Plumbers	
Pipe Fitters	
Sheet Metal	
Truck Drivers	
Total	

Equipment	Hrs.

Material Purchased

30 OCT. 20____   DAILY LOG   DAY _____

CONTRACTOR _____ JOB NAME _____ JOB NO._____

Work Performed Today _____

_____

_____

_____

_____

_____

_____

_____

_____

_____

_____

_____

_____

_____

Problems - Delays _____

_____

_____

_____

Sub-Contractor Progress _____

_____

_____

_____

Special Assignments _____

_____

_____

Weather	
Temp. AM _____ PM _____	
Safety Meeting _____	

Work Force	No.
Superintendent	_____
Clerk	_____
Bricklayers	_____
Carpenters	_____
Cement Masons	_____
Electricians	_____
Iron Workers	_____
Laborers	_____
Operating Eng.	_____
Plumbers	_____
Pipe Fitters	_____
Sheet Metal	_____
Truck Drivers	_____
Total	_____

Equipment	Hrs.

Extra Work	Authorized By	Approx. Price

Equipment Rented Today	Rented From	Rate

Material Purchased

Supervisor's Signature _____

DAY _____   DAILY LOG   20___ OCT. 31

CONTRACTOR _____ JOB NAME _____ JOB NO _____

Work Performed Today _____

_____

_____

_____

_____

_____

_____

_____

_____

_____

_____

_____

_____

_____

Problems - Delays _____

_____

_____

_____

Sub-Contractor Progress _____

_____

_____

_____

Special Assignments _____

_____

_____

Weather	_____	
Temp. AM _____ PM _____		
Safety Meeting _____		

Work Force	No.
Superintendent	_____
Clerk	_____
Bricklayers	_____
Carpenters	_____
Cement Masons	_____
Electricians	_____
Iron Workers	_____
Laborers	_____
Operating Eng.	_____
Plumbers	_____
Pipe Fitters	_____
Sheet Metal	_____
Truck Drivers	_____
Total	_____

Equipment	Hrs.

Extra Work	Authorized By	Approx. Price

Equipment Rented Today	Rented From	Rate

Material Purchased

Supervisor's Signature _____

1 NOV. 20___   DAILY LOG   DAY _____

CONTRACTOR _____ JOB NAME _____ JOB NO._____

Work Performed Today _____

_____

_____

_____

_____

_____

_____

_____

_____

_____

_____

_____

_____

Problems - Delays _____

_____

_____

_____

Sub-Contractor Progress _____

_____

_____

_____

Special Assignments _____

_____

_____

| Weather | _____ |
| Temp. AM _____PM _____ | |

| Safety Meeting _____ | |

Work Force	No.
Superintendent	_____
Clerk	_____
Bricklayers	_____
Carpenters	_____
Cement Masons	_____
Electricians	_____
Iron Workers	_____
Laborers	_____
Operating Eng.	_____
Plumbers	_____
Pipe Fitters	_____
Sheet Metal	_____
Truck Drivers	_____
Total	_____

Equipment	Hrs.

Extra Work	Authorized By	Approx. Price

Equipment Rented Today	Rented From	Rate

Material Purchased

Supervisor's Signature _____

DAY _____   DAILY LOG   20___ NOV. 2

CONTRACTOR _____ JOB NAME _____ JOB NO _____

Work Performed Today _____	Weather _____
_____	Temp. AM _____PM _____
_____	Safety Meeting _____

Work Force	No.
Superintendent	_____
Clerk	_____
Bricklayers	_____
Carpenters	_____
Cement Masons	_____
Electricians	_____
Iron Workers	_____
Laborers	_____
Operating Eng.	_____
Plumbers	_____
Pipe Fitters	_____
Sheet Metal	_____
Truck Drivers	_____
Total	_____

Work Performed Today lines (continued):
_____
_____
_____
_____
_____
_____
_____

Problems - Delays _____
_____
_____
_____

Sub-Contractor Progress _____
_____
_____
_____

Equipment	Hrs.

Special Assignments _____
_____
_____

Extra Work	Authorized By	Approx. Price

Equipment Rented Today	Rented From	Rate

Material Purchased

Supervisor's Signature _____

3 NOV. 20___   DAILY LOG   DAY _____

CONTRACTOR _____ JOB NAME _____ JOB NO._____

Work Performed Today _____

_____

_____

_____

_____

_____

_____

_____

_____

_____

_____

_____

_____

_____

Problems - Delays _____

_____

_____

_____

Sub-Contractor Progress _____

_____

_____

_____

Special Assignments _____

_____

_____

Extra Work	Authorized By	Approx. Price

Equipment Rented Today	Rented From	Rate

Supervisor's Signature _____

Weather _____

Temp. AM _____PM _____

Safety Meeting _____

Work Force	No.
Superintendent	
Clerk	
Bricklayers	
Carpenters	
Cement Masons	
Electricians	
Iron Workers	
Laborers	
Operating Eng.	
Plumbers	
Pipe Fitters	
Sheet Metal	
Truck Drivers	
Total	

Equipment	Hrs.

Material Purchased

DAY _____   DAILY LOG   20___ NOV. 4

CONTRACTOR _____ JOB NAME _____ JOB NO _____

Work Performed Today _____

_____

_____

_____

_____

_____

_____

_____

_____

_____

_____

_____

_____

_____

_____

Problems - Delays _____

_____

_____

_____

Sub-Contractor Progress _____

_____

_____

Special Assignments _____

_____

_____

| Weather | _____ |
| Temp. AM _____ PM ____ |
| Safety Meeting _____ |

Work Force	No.
Superintendent	____
Clerk	____
Bricklayers	____
Carpenters	____
Cement Masons	____
Electricians	____
Iron Workers	____
Laborers	____
Operating Eng.	____
Plumbers	____
Pipe Fitters	____
Sheet Metal	____
Truck Drivers	____
Total	____

Equipment	Hrs.

Material Purchased

Extra Work	Authorized By	Approx. Price

Equipment Rented Today	Rented From	Rate

Supervisor's Signature _____

5 NOV. 20___   DAILY LOG   DAY _____

CONTRACTOR _____ JOB NAME _____ JOB NO._____

Work Performed Today _____

_____

_____

_____

_____

_____

_____

_____

_____

_____

_____

_____

_____

Problems - Delays _____

_____

_____

Sub-Contractor Progress _____

_____

_____

_____

Special Assignments _____

_____

_____

_____

Weather	_____
Temp. AM _____ PM _____	
Safety Meeting _____	

Work Force	No.
Superintendent	_____
Clerk	_____
Bricklayers	_____
Carpenters	_____
Cement Masons	_____
Electricians	_____
Iron Workers	_____
Laborers	_____
Operating Eng.	_____
Plumbers	_____
Pipe Fitters	_____
Sheet Metal	_____
Truck Drivers	_____
Total	_____

Equipment	Hrs.

Material Purchased	

Extra Work	Authorized By	Approx. Price

Equipment Rented Today	Rented From	Rate

Supervisor's Signature _____

DAY _____   DAILY LOG   20___ NOV. 6

CONTRACTOR _____ JOB NAME _____ JOB NO _____

Work Performed Today _____

_____

_____

_____

_____

_____

_____

_____

_____

_____

_____

_____

_____

_____

Problems - Delays _____

_____

_____

_____

Sub-Contractor Progress _____

_____

_____

_____

Special Assignments _____

_____

_____

| Weather _____ |
| Temp. AM _____PM _____ |
| Safety Meeting _____ |

Work Force	No.
Superintendent	_____
Clerk	_____
Bricklayers	_____
Carpenters	_____
Cement Masons	_____
Electricians	_____
Iron Workers	_____
Laborers	_____
Operating Eng.	_____
Plumbers	_____
Pipe Fitters	_____
Sheet Metal	_____
Truck Drivers	_____
Total	_____

Equipment	Hrs.

Material Purchased	

Extra Work	Authorized By	Approx. Price

Equipment Rented Today	Rented From	Rate

Supervisor's Signature _____

7 NOV. 20___   DAILY LOG   DAY _____

CONTRACTOR _____ JOB NAME _____ JOB NO._____

Work Performed Today _____	Weather _____
_____	Temp. AM _____PM _____
_____	Safety Meeting _____

Work Force	No.
Superintendent	_____
Clerk	_____
Bricklayers	_____
Carpenters	_____
Cement Masons	_____
Electricians	_____
Iron Workers	_____
Laborers	_____
Operating Eng.	_____
Plumbers	_____
Pipe Fitters	_____
Sheet Metal	_____
Truck Drivers	_____
Total	_____

Problems - Delays _____

Sub-Contractor Progress _____

Equipment	Hrs.

Special Assignments _____

Extra Work	Authorized By	Approx. Price

Equipment Rented Today	Rented From	Rate

Material Purchased

Supervisor's Signature _____

DAY _____ DAILY LOG 20___ NOV. 8

CONTRACTOR _____ JOB NAME _____ JOB NO _____

Work Performed Today _____

_____

_____

_____

_____

_____

_____

_____

_____

_____

_____

_____

_____

_____

Problems - Delays _____

_____

_____

_____

Sub-Contractor Progress _____

_____

_____

_____

Special Assignments _____

_____

_____

Weather	_____
Temp. AM _____ PM _____	
Safety Meeting _____	

Work Force	No.
Superintendent	_____
Clerk	_____
Bricklayers	_____
Carpenters	_____
Cement Masons	_____
Electricians	_____
Iron Workers	_____
Laborers	_____
Operating Eng.	_____
Plumbers	_____
Pipe Fitters	_____
Sheet Metal	_____
Truck Drivers	_____
Total	_____

Equipment	Hrs.

Material Purchased	

Extra Work	Authorized By	Approx. Price

Equipment Rented Today	Rented From	Rate

Supervisor's Signature _____

9 NOV. 20___   DAILY LOG   DAY _____

CONTRACTOR _____ JOB NAME _____ JOB NO._____

Work Performed Today _____	Weather _____
	Temp. AM _____PM _____
	Safety Meeting _____

Work Force	No.
Superintendent	_____
Clerk	_____
Bricklayers	_____
Carpenters	_____
Cement Masons	_____
Electricians	_____
Iron Workers	_____
Laborers	_____
Operating Eng.	_____
Plumbers	_____
Pipe Fitters	_____
Sheet Metal	_____
Truck Drivers	_____
Total	_____

Problems - Delays _____

Sub-Contractor Progress _____

Special Assignments _____

Equipment	Hrs.

Extra Work	Authorized By	Approx. Price

Equipment Rented Today	Rented From	Rate

Material Purchased

Supervisor's Signature _____

DAY _____   DAILY LOG   20____ NOV. 10

CONTRACTOR _____ JOB NAME _____ JOB NO _____

Work Performed Today _____

_____

_____

_____

_____

_____

_____

_____

_____

_____

_____

_____

_____

_____

_____

Problems - Delays _____

_____

_____

_____

Sub-Contractor Progress _____

_____

_____

_____

Special Assignments _____

_____

_____

Extra Work	Authorized By	Approx. Price

Equipment Rented Today	Rented From	Rate

Supervisor's Signature _____

Weather _____

Temp. AM _____PM _____

Safety Meeting _____

Work Force	No.
Superintendent	____
Clerk	____
Bricklayers	____
Carpenters	____
Cement Masons	____
Electricians	____
Iron Workers	____
Laborers	____
Operating Eng.	____
Plumbers	____
Pipe Fitters	____
Sheet Metal	____
Truck Drivers	____
Total	____

Equipment	Hrs.

Material Purchased

11 NOV. 20___   DAILY LOG   DAY _____

CONTRACTOR _____ JOB NAME _____ JOB NO._____

Work Performed Today _____	Weather _____
_____	Temp. AM _____PM _____
_____	Safety Meeting _____

Work Force	No.
Superintendent	_____
Clerk	_____
Bricklayers	_____
Carpenters	_____
Cement Masons	_____
Electricians	_____
Iron Workers	_____
Laborers	_____
Operating Eng.	_____
Plumbers	_____
Pipe Fitters	_____
Sheet Metal	_____
Truck Drivers	_____
Total	_____

Problems - Delays _____

Equipment	Hrs.

Sub-Contractor Progress _____

Special Assignments _____

Material Purchased	

Extra Work	Authorized By	Approx. Price

Equipment Rented Today	Rented From	Rate

Supervisor's Signature _____

DAY _____   DAILY LOG   20___ NOV. 12

CONTRACTOR _____ JOB NAME _____ JOB NO _____

Work Performed Today _____

_____

_____

_____

_____

_____

_____

_____

_____

_____

_____

_____

_____

Problems - Delays _____

_____

_____

_____

Sub-Contractor Progress _____

_____

_____

_____

Special Assignments _____

_____

_____

| Weather |
| Temp. AM _____ PM _____ |
| Safety Meeting _____ |

Work Force	No.
Superintendent	_____
Clerk	_____
Bricklayers	_____
Carpenters	_____
Cement Masons	_____
Electricians	_____
Iron Workers	_____
Laborers	_____
Operating Eng.	_____
Plumbers	_____
Pipe Fitters	_____
Sheet Metal	_____
Truck Drivers	_____
Total	_____

Equipment	Hrs.

Extra Work	Authorized By	Approx. Price

Equipment Rented Today	Rented From	Rate

Material Purchased

Supervisor's Signature _____

13 NOV. 20___   DAILY LOG   DAY _____

CONTRACTOR _____ JOB NAME _____ JOB NO._____

Work Performed Today _____

_____

_____

_____

_____

_____

_____

_____

_____

_____

_____

_____

_____

_____

Problems - Delays _____

_____

_____

_____

Sub-Contractor Progress _____

_____

_____

_____

Special Assignments _____

_____

_____

_____

| Weather | _____ |
| Temp. AM _____PM _____ | |

| Safety Meeting _____ | |

Work Force	**No.**
Superintendent	_____
Clerk	_____
Bricklayers	_____
Carpenters	_____
Cement Masons	_____
Electricians	_____
Iron Workers	_____
Laborers	_____
Operating Eng.	_____
Plumbers	_____
Pipe Fitters	_____
Sheet Metal	_____
Truck Drivers	_____
Total	_____

Equipment	Hrs.

Material Purchased	

Extra Work	Authorized By	Approx. Price

Equipment Rented Today	Rented From	Rate

Supervisor's Signature _____

DAY _____   DAILY LOG   20___ NOV. 14

CONTRACTOR _____ JOB NAME _____ JOB NO _____

Work Performed Today _____

_____

_____

_____

_____

_____

_____

_____

_____

_____

_____

_____

_____

Problems - Delays _____

_____

_____

_____

Sub-Contractor Progress _____

_____

_____

_____

Special Assignments _____

_____

_____

| Weather _____ |
| Temp. AM _____ PM _____ |
| Safety Meeting _____ |

Work Force	No.
Superintendent	_____
Clerk	_____
Bricklayers	_____
Carpenters	_____
Cement Masons	_____
Electricians	_____
Iron Workers	_____
Laborers	_____
Operating Eng.	_____
Plumbers	_____
Pipe Fitters	_____
Sheet Metal	_____
Truck Drivers	_____
Total	_____

Equipment	Hrs.

Extra Work	Authorized By	Approx. Price

Equipment Rented Today	Rented From	Rate

Material Purchased

Supervisor's Signature _____

15 NOV. 20___   DAILY LOG   DAY _____

CONTRACTOR _____   JOB NAME _____   JOB NO. _____

Work Performed Today	Weather _____
	Temp. AM _____ PM _____
	Safety Meeting _____

Work Force	No.
Superintendent	_____
Clerk	_____
Bricklayers	_____
Carpenters	_____
Cement Masons	_____
Electricians	_____
Iron Workers	_____
Laborers	_____
Operating Eng.	_____
Plumbers	_____
Pipe Fitters	_____
Sheet Metal	_____
Truck Drivers	_____
Total	_____

Problems - Delays _____

Equipment	Hrs.

Sub-Contractor Progress _____

Special Assignments _____

Extra Work	Authorized By	Approx. Price

Equipment Rented Today	Rented From	Rate

Material Purchased

Supervisor's Signature _____

DAY _____   DAILY LOG   20___ NOV. 16

CONTRACTOR _____ JOB NAME _____ JOB NO _____

Work Performed Today _____

_____

_____

_____

_____

_____

_____

_____

_____

_____

_____

_____

Problems - Delays _____

_____

_____

_____

Sub-Contractor Progress _____

_____

_____

Special Assignments _____

_____

_____

Weather	_____	
Temp. AM _____ PM _____		
Safety Meeting _____		

Work Force	No.
Superintendent	_____
Clerk	_____
Bricklayers	_____
Carpenters	_____
Cement Masons	_____
Electricians	_____
Iron Workers	_____
Laborers	_____
Operating Eng.	_____
Plumbers	_____
Pipe Fitters	_____
Sheet Metal	_____
Truck Drivers	_____
Total	_____

Equipment	Hrs.

Extra Work	Authorized By	Approx. Price

Equipment Rented Today	Rented From	Rate

Material Purchased

Supervisor's Signature _____

17 NOV. 20___   DAILY LOG   DAY _____

CONTRACTOR _____ JOB NAME _____ JOB NO._____

Work Performed Today _____

_____

_____

_____

_____

_____

_____

_____

_____

_____

_____

_____

_____

Problems - Delays _____

_____

_____

_____

Sub-Contractor Progress _____

_____

_____

Special Assignments _____

_____

_____

Weather	_____	
Temp. AM _____ PM _____		

Safety Meeting _____

Work Force	No.
Superintendent	_____
Clerk	_____
Bricklayers	_____
Carpenters	_____
Cement Masons	_____
Electricians	_____
Iron Workers	_____
Laborers	_____
Operating Eng.	_____
Plumbers	_____
Pipe Fitters	_____
Sheet Metal	_____
Truck Drivers	_____
Total	_____

Equipment	Hrs.

Material Purchased	

Extra Work	Authorized By	Approx. Price

Equipment Rented Today	Rented From	Rate

Supervisor's Signature _____

DAY _____   DAILY LOG   20___ NOV. 18

CONTRACTOR _____ JOB NAME _____ JOB NO _____

Work Performed Today _____

_____

_____

_____

_____

_____

_____

_____

_____

_____

_____

_____

_____

_____

_____

Problems - Delays _____

_____

_____

_____

Sub-Contractor Progress _____

_____

_____

Special Assignments _____

_____

_____

Weather	
Temp. AM _____ PM _____	
Safety Meeting _____	

Work Force	No.
Superintendent	_____
Clerk	_____
Bricklayers	_____
Carpenters	_____
Cement Masons	_____
Electricians	_____
Iron Workers	_____
Laborers	_____
Operating Eng.	_____
Plumbers	_____
Pipe Fitters	_____
Sheet Metal	
Truck Drivers	
Total	_____

Equipment	Hrs.

Extra Work	Authorized By	Approx. Price

Equipment Rented Today	Rented From	Rate

Material Purchased

Supervisor's Signature _____

19 NOV. 20____   DAILY LOG   DAY _____

CONTRACTOR _____ JOB NAME _____ JOB NO._____

Work Performed Today _____

_____

_____

_____

_____

_____

_____

_____

_____

_____

_____

_____

Problems - Delays _____

_____

_____

_____

Sub-Contractor Progress _____

_____

_____

_____

Special Assignments _____

_____

_____

Extra Work	Authorized By	Approx. Price

Equipment Rented Today	Rented From	Rate

Supervisor's Signature _____

Weather _____

Temp. AM _____ PM _____

Safety Meeting _____

Work Force	No.
Superintendent	_____
Clerk	_____
Bricklayers	_____
Carpenters	_____
Cement Masons	_____
Electricians	_____
Iron Workers	_____
Laborers	_____
Operating Eng.	_____
Plumbers	_____
Pipe Fitters	_____
Sheet Metal	_____
Truck Drivers	_____
Total	_____

Equipment	Hrs.

Material Purchased

DAY _____   DAILY LOG   20___ NOV. 20

CONTRACTOR _____ JOB NAME _____ JOB NO _____

Work Performed Today _____	Weather _____
	Temp. AM _____PM _____
	Safety Meeting _____

Work Force	No.
Superintendent	_____
Clerk	_____
Bricklayers	_____
Carpenters	_____
Cement Masons	_____
Electricians	_____
Iron Workers	_____
Laborers	_____
Operating Eng.	_____
Plumbers	_____
Pipe Fitters	_____
Sheet Metal	_____
Truck Drivers	_____
Total	_____

Problems - Delays _____

Equipment	Hrs.

Sub-Contractor Progress _____

Special Assignments _____

Extra Work	Authorized By	Approx. Price

Material Purchased	

Equipment Rented Today	Rented From	Rate

Supervisor's Signature _____

21 NOV. 20____   DAILY LOG   DAY _____

CONTRACTOR _____ JOB NAME _____ JOB NO._____

Work Performed Today _____

_____

_____

_____

_____

_____

_____

_____

_____

_____

_____

_____

_____

_____

Problems - Delays _____

_____

_____

_____

Sub-Contractor Progress _____

_____

_____

_____

Special Assignments _____

_____

_____

_____

Extra Work	Authorized By	Approx. Price

Equipment Rented Today	Rented From	Rate

Supervisor's Signature _____

Weather _____

Temp. AM _____PM _____

Safety Meeting _____

Work Force	No.
Superintendent	_____
Clerk	_____
Bricklayers	_____
Carpenters	_____
Cement Masons	_____
Electricians	_____
Iron Workers	_____
Laborers	_____
Operating Eng.	_____
Plumbers	_____
Pipe Fitters	_____
Sheet Metal	_____
Truck Drivers	_____
Total	_____

Equipment	Hrs.

Material Purchased

DAY _____   DAILY LOG   20___ NOV. 22

CONTRACTOR _____ JOB NAME _____ JOB NO _____

Work Performed Today _____

_____

_____

_____

_____

_____

_____

_____

_____

_____

_____

_____

_____

Problems - Delays _____

_____

_____

_____

Sub-Contractor Progress _____

_____

_____

_____

Special Assignments _____

_____

_____

Extra Work	Authorized By	Approx. Price

Equipment Rented Today	Rented From	Rate

Supervisor's Signature _____

Weather _____

Temp. AM _____ PM _____

Safety Meeting _____

Work Force	No.
Superintendent	_____
Clerk	_____
Bricklayers	_____
Carpenters	_____
Cement Masons	_____
Electricians	_____
Iron Workers	_____
Laborers	_____
Operating Eng.	_____
Plumbers	_____
Pipe Fitters	_____
Sheet Metal	_____
Truck Drivers	_____
Total	_____

Equipment	Hrs.

Material Purchased

23 NOV. 20___   DAILY LOG   DAY _____

CONTRACTOR _____ JOB NAME _____ JOB NO._____

Work Performed Today _____

_____

_____

_____

_____

_____

_____

_____

_____

_____

Problems - Delays _____

_____

_____

_____

Sub-Contractor Progress _____

_____

_____

Special Assignments _____

_____

Extra Work	Authorized By	Approx. Price

Equipment Rented Today	Rented From	Rate

Supervisor's Signature _____

Weather _____

Temp. AM _____PM _____

Safety Meeting _____

Work Force	No.
Superintendent	_____
Clerk	_____
Bricklayers	_____
Carpenters	_____
Cement Masons	_____
Electricians	_____
Iron Workers	_____
Laborers	_____
Operating Eng.	_____
Plumbers	_____
Pipe Fitters	_____
Sheet Metal	_____
Truck Drivers	_____
Total	_____

Equipment	Hrs.

Material Purchased

DAY _____   DAILY LOG   20___ NOV. 24

CONTRACTOR _____ JOB NAME _____ JOB NO _____

Work Performed Today _____

_____

_____

_____

_____

_____

_____

_____

_____

_____

_____

_____

_____

Problems - Delays _____

_____

_____

_____

Sub-Contractor Progress _____

_____

_____

Special Assignments _____

_____

_____

Weather _____

Temp. AM _____ PM _____

Safety Meeting _____

Work Force	No.
Superintendent	_____
Clerk	_____
Bricklayers	_____
Carpenters	_____
Cement Masons	_____
Electricians	_____
Iron Workers	_____
Laborers	_____
Operating Eng.	_____
Plumbers	_____
Pipe Fitters	_____
Sheet Metal	_____
Truck Drivers	_____
Total	_____

Equipment	Hrs.

Extra Work	Authorized By	Approx. Price

Equipment Rented Today	Rented From	Rate

Material Purchased

Supervisor's Signature _____

25 NOV. 20____   DAILY LOG   DAY _____

CONTRACTOR _____ JOB NAME _____ JOB NO._____

Work Performed Today _____

_____

_____

_____

_____

_____

_____

_____

_____

_____

_____

_____

_____

Problems - Delays _____

_____

_____

_____

Sub-Contractor Progress _____

_____

_____

_____

Special Assignments _____

_____

Weather	_____
Temp. AM _____ PM _____	
Safety Meeting _____	

Work Force	No.
Superintendent	_____
Clerk	_____
Bricklayers	_____
Carpenters	_____
Cement Masons	_____
Electricians	_____
Iron Workers	_____
Laborers	_____
Operating Eng.	_____
Plumbers	_____
Pipe Fitters	_____
Sheet Metal	_____
Truck Drivers	_____
Total	_____

Equipment	Hrs.

Extra Work	Authorized By	Approx. Price

Equipment Rented Today	Rented From	Rate

Material Purchased

Supervisor's Signature _____

DAY _____   DAILY LOG   20___ NOV. 26

CONTRACTOR _____ JOB NAME _____ JOB NO _____

Work Performed Today _____

_____

_____

_____

_____

_____

_____

_____

_____

_____

_____

_____

_____

Problems - Delays _____

_____

_____

_____

Sub-Contractor Progress _____

_____

_____

_____

Special Assignments _____

_____

_____

Weather		
Temp. AM _____ PM _____		
Safety Meeting _____		

Work Force	No.
Superintendent	_____
Clerk	_____
Bricklayers	_____
Carpenters	_____
Cement Masons	_____
Electricians	_____
Iron Workers	_____
Laborers	_____
Operating Eng.	_____
Plumbers	_____
Pipe Fitters	_____
Sheet Metal	_____
Truck Drivers	_____
Total	_____

Equipment	Hrs.

Material Purchased

Extra Work	Authorized By	Approx. Price

Equipment Rented Today	Rented From	Rate

Supervisor's Signature _____

27 NOV. 20___   DAILY LOG   DAY _____

CONTRACTOR _____ JOB NAME _____ JOB NO._____

Work Performed Today _____	Weather _____
	Temp. AM _____ PM _____
	Safety Meeting _____

Work Force	No.
Superintendent	_____
Clerk	_____
Bricklayers	_____
Carpenters	_____
Cement Masons	_____
Electricians	_____
Iron Workers	_____
Laborers	_____
Operating Eng.	_____
Plumbers	_____
Pipe Fitters	_____
Sheet Metal	_____
Truck Drivers	_____
Total	_____

Problems - Delays _____

Equipment	Hrs.

Sub-Contractor Progress _____

Special Assignments _____

Extra Work	Authorized By	Approx. Price

Equipment Rented Today	Rented From	Rate

Material Purchased

Supervisor's Signature _____

DAY _____   DAILY LOG   20____ NOV. 28

CONTRACTOR _____ JOB NAME _____ JOB NO _____

Work Performed Today _____	Weather _____
	Temp. AM _____ PM _____
	Safety Meeting _____

Work Force	No.
Superintendent	_____
Clerk	_____
Bricklayers	_____
Carpenters	_____
Cement Masons	_____
Electricians	_____
Iron Workers	_____
Laborers	_____
Operating Eng.	_____
Plumbers	_____
Pipe Fitters	_____
Sheet Metal	_____
Truck Drivers	_____
Total	_____

Problems - Delays _____

Equipment	Hrs.

Sub-Contractor Progress _____

Special Assignments _____

Extra Work	Authorized By	Approx. Price

Equipment Rented Today	Rented From	Rate

Material Purchased

Supervisor's Signature _____

29 NOV. 20___   DAILY LOG   DAY _____

CONTRACTOR _____ JOB NAME _____ JOB NO._____

Work Performed Today _____	Weather _____
_____	Temp. AM _____ PM _____
_____	Safety Meeting _____

	Work Force	No.
	Superintendent	_____
	Clerk	_____
	Bricklayers	_____
	Carpenters	_____
	Cement Masons	_____
	Electricians	_____
	Iron Workers	_____
	Laborers	_____
	Operating Eng.	_____
	Plumbers	_____
	Pipe Fitters	_____
	Sheet Metal	_____
	Truck Drivers	_____
	Total	_____

Problems - Delays _____
_____
_____
_____

Sub-Contractor Progress _____
_____
_____
_____

Equipment	Hrs.

Special Assignments _____
_____
_____

Extra Work	Authorized By	Approx. Price

Equipment Rented Today	Rented From	Rate

Material Purchased

Supervisor's Signature _____

DAY _____   DAILY LOG   20____ NOV. 30

CONTRACTOR _____ JOB NAME _____ JOB NO _____

| Work Performed Today _____ | Weather _____ |
| | Temp. AM _____ PM _____ |

Safety Meeting _____

Work Force	No.
Superintendent	_____
Clerk	_____
Bricklayers	_____
Carpenters	_____
Cement Masons	_____
Electricians	_____
Iron Workers	_____
Laborers	_____
Operating Eng.	_____
Plumbers	_____
Pipe Fitters	_____
Sheet Metal	_____
Truck Drivers	_____
Total	_____

Problems - Delays _____

Equipment	Hrs.

Sub-Contractor Progress _____

Special Assignments _____

Material Purchased

Extra Work	Authorized By	Approx. Price

Equipment Rented Today	Rented From	Rate

Supervisor's Signature _____

1 DEC. 20___   DAILY LOG   DAY _____

CONTRACTOR _____ JOB NAME _____ JOB NO._____

Work Performed Today _____	Weather _____
_____	Temp. AM _____PM _____
_____	Safety Meeting _____
_____	**Work Force** **No.**
_____	Superintendent _____
_____	Clerk _____
_____	Bricklayers _____
_____	Carpenters _____
_____	Cement Masons _____
_____	Electricians _____
_____	Iron Workers _____
_____	Laborers _____
_____	Operating Eng. _____
_____	Plumbers _____
_____	Pipe Fitters _____
_____	Sheet Metal _____
_____	Truck Drivers _____

Problems - Delays _____
_____
_____
_____

Total _____

Sub-Contractor Progress _____
_____
_____
_____

Equipment	Hrs.

Special Assignments _____
_____
_____

Extra Work	Authorized By	Approx. Price

Equipment Rented Today	Rented From	Rate

Material Purchased

Supervisor's Signature _____

DAY _____   DAILY LOG   20___ DEC. 2

CONTRACTOR _____ JOB NAME _____ JOB NO _____

Work Performed Today _____	Weather _____
	Temp. AM _____ PM _____
	Safety Meeting _____

Work Force	No.
Superintendent	_____
Clerk	_____
Bricklayers	_____
Carpenters	_____
Cement Masons	_____
Electricians	_____
Iron Workers	_____
Laborers	_____
Operating Eng.	_____
Plumbers	_____
Pipe Fitters	_____
Sheet Metal	_____
Truck Drivers	_____
Total	_____

Problems - Delays _____

Equipment	Hrs.

Sub-Contractor Progress _____

Special Assignments _____

Material Purchased

Extra Work	Authorized By	Approx. Price

Equipment Rented Today	Rented From	Rate

Supervisor's Signature _____

3 DEC. 20___   DAILY LOG   DAY _____

CONTRACTOR _____ JOB NAME _____ JOB NO._____

Work Performed Today _____	Weather _____

Work Performed Today _____

_____

_____

_____

_____

_____

_____

_____

_____

_____

_____

_____

_____

Problems - Delays _____

_____

_____

_____

Sub-Contractor Progress _____

_____

_____

_____

Special Assignments _____

_____

_____

Weather _____

Temp. AM _____ PM _____

Safety Meeting _____

Work Force	No.
Superintendent	_____
Clerk	_____
Bricklayers	_____
Carpenters	_____
Cement Masons	_____
Electricians	_____
Iron Workers	_____
Laborers	_____
Operating Eng.	_____
Plumbers	_____
Pipe Fitters	_____
Sheet Metal	_____
Truck Drivers	_____
Total	_____

Equipment	Hrs.

Extra Work	Authorized By	Approx. Price

Equipment Rented Today	Rented From	Rate

Material Purchased

Supervisor's Signature _____

DAY _____   DAILY LOG   20____ DEC. 4

CONTRACTOR _____ JOB NAME _____ JOB NO _____

Work Performed Today _____

_____

_____

_____

_____

_____

_____

_____

_____

_____

_____

_____

_____

Problems - Delays _____

_____

_____

_____

Sub-Contractor Progress _____

_____

_____

_____

Special Assignments _____

_____

_____

| Weather _____ |
| Temp. AM _____ PM _____ |
| Safety Meeting _____ |

Work Force	No.
Superintendent	_____
Clerk	_____
Bricklayers	_____
Carpenters	_____
Cement Masons	_____
Electricians	_____
Iron Workers	_____
Laborers	_____
Operating Eng.	_____
Plumbers	_____
Pipe Fitters	_____
Sheet Metal	_____
Truck Drivers	_____
Total	_____

Equipment	Hrs.

Extra Work	Authorized By	Approx. Price

Equipment Rented Today	Rented From	Rate

Material Purchased

Supervisor's Signature _____

5 DEC. 20___   DAILY LOG   DAY _____

CONTRACTOR _____ JOB NAME _____ JOB NO._____

Work Performed Today _____

_____

_____

_____

_____

_____

_____

_____

_____

_____

_____

_____

_____

Problems - Delays _____

_____

_____

_____

Sub-Contractor Progress _____

_____

_____

Special Assignments _____

_____

_____

| Weather | _____ |
| Temp. AM _____PM _____ | |

| Safety Meeting _____ | |

Work Force	No.
Superintendent	_____
Clerk	_____
Bricklayers	_____
Carpenters	_____
Cement Masons	_____
Electricians	_____
Iron Workers	_____
Laborers	_____
Operating Eng.	_____
Plumbers	_____
Pipe Fitters	_____
Sheet Metal	_____
Truck Drivers	_____
Total	_____

Equipment	Hrs.

Material Purchased	

Extra Work	Authorized By	Approx. Price

Equipment Rented Today	Rented From	Rate

Supervisor's Signature _____

DAY _____   DAILY LOG   20____ DEC. 6

CONTRACTOR _____ JOB NAME _____ JOB NO _____

Work Performed Today _____

_____

_____

_____

_____

_____

_____

_____

_____

_____

_____

_____

Problems - Delays _____

_____

_____

_____

Sub-Contractor Progress _____

_____

_____

_____

Special Assignments _____

_____

_____

| Weather _____ |
| Temp. AM _____ PM _____ |
| Safety Meeting _____ |

Work Force	No.
Superintendent	_____
Clerk	_____
Bricklayers	_____
Carpenters	_____
Cement Masons	_____
Electricians	_____
Iron Workers	_____
Laborers	_____
Operating Eng.	_____
Plumbers	_____
Pipe Fitters	_____
Sheet Metal	_____
Truck Drivers	_____
Total	_____

Equipment	Hrs.

Extra Work	Authorized By	Approx. Price

Equipment Rented Today	Rented From	Rate

Material Purchased

Supervisor's Signature _____

7 DEC. 20___   DAILY LOG   DAY _____

CONTRACTOR _____ JOB NAME _____ JOB NO._____

Work Performed Today _____

_____

_____

_____

_____

_____

_____

_____

_____

_____

_____

_____

_____

_____

Problems - Delays _____

_____

_____

_____

Sub-Contractor Progress _____

_____

_____

_____

Special Assignments _____

_____

_____

Extra Work	Authorized By	Approx. Price

Equipment Rented Today	Rented From	Rate

Supervisor's Signature _____

Weather _____

Temp. AM _____PM _____

Safety Meeting _____

Work Force	No.
Superintendent	
Clerk	
Bricklayers	
Carpenters	
Cement Masons	
Electricians	
Iron Workers	
Laborers	
Operating Eng.	
Plumbers	
Pipe Fitters	
Sheet Metal	
Truck Drivers	
Total	

Equipment	Hrs.

Material Purchased

DAY _____   DAILY LOG   20___ DEC. 8

CONTRACTOR _____ JOB NAME _____ JOB NO _____

Work Performed Today _____

_____

_____

_____

_____

_____

_____

_____

_____

_____

_____

_____

_____

Problems - Delays _____

_____

_____

_____

Sub-Contractor Progress _____

_____

_____

Special Assignments _____

_____

_____

Weather	
Temp. AM _____ PM _____	
Safety Meeting _____	

Work Force	No.
Superintendent	_____
Clerk	_____
Bricklayers	_____
Carpenters	_____
Cement Masons	_____
Electricians	_____
Iron Workers	_____
Laborers	_____
Operating Eng.	_____
Plumbers	_____
Pipe Fitters	_____
Sheet Metal	_____
Truck Drivers	_____
Total	_____

Equipment	Hrs.

Extra Work	Authorized By	Approx. Price

Equipment Rented Today	Rented From	Rate

Material Purchased

Supervisor's Signature _____

9 DEC. 20____   DAILY LOG   DAY _____

CONTRACTOR _____ JOB NAME _____ JOB NO._____

Work Performed Today _____

_____

_____

_____

_____

_____

_____

_____

_____

_____

_____

_____

_____

_____

Problems - Delays _____

_____

_____

_____

Sub-Contractor Progress _____

_____

_____

_____

Special Assignments _____

_____

_____

Extra Work	Authorized By	Approx. Price

Equipment Rented Today	Rented From	Rate

Supervisor's Signature _____

Weather _____

Temp. AM _____PM _____

Safety Meeting _____

Work Force	No.
Superintendent	_____
Clerk	_____
Bricklayers	_____
Carpenters	_____
Cement Masons	_____
Electricians	_____
Iron Workers	_____
Laborers	_____
Operating Eng.	_____
Plumbers	_____
Pipe Fitters	_____
Sheet Metal	_____
Truck Drivers	_____
Total	_____

Equipment	Hrs.

Material Purchased

DAY _____   DAILY LOG   20___ DEC. 10

CONTRACTOR _____ JOB NAME _____ JOB NO _____

Work Performed Today _____

_____

_____

_____

_____

_____

_____

_____

_____

_____

_____

_____

_____

Problems - Delays _____

_____

_____

_____

Sub-Contractor Progress _____

_____

_____

Special Assignments _____

_____

_____

| Weather _____ |
| Temp. AM _____PM _____ |
| Safety Meeting _____ |

Work Force	No.
Superintendent	_____
Clerk	_____
Bricklayers	_____
Carpenters	_____
Cement Masons	_____
Electricians	_____
Iron Workers	_____
Laborers	_____
Operating Eng.	_____
Plumbers	_____
Pipe Fitters	_____
Sheet Metal	_____
Truck Drivers	_____
Total	_____

Equipment	Hrs.

Material Purchased	

Extra Work	Authorized By	Approx. Price

Equipment Rented Today	Rented From	Rate

Supervisor's Signature _____

11 DEC. 20___   DAILY LOG   DAY _____

CONTRACTOR _____ JOB NAME _____ JOB NO._____

Work Performed Today _____	Weather _____
_____	Temp. AM _____PM _____
_____	Safety Meeting _____

	Work Force	**No.**
	Superintendent	_____
	Clerk	_____
	Bricklayers	_____
	Carpenters	_____
	Cement Masons	_____
	Electricians	_____
	Iron Workers	_____
	Laborers	_____
	Operating Eng.	_____
	Plumbers	_____
	Pipe Fitters	_____
	Sheet Metal	_____
	Truck Drivers	_____
	Total	_____

Problems - Delays _____

Equipment	Hrs.

Sub-Contractor Progress _____

Special Assignments _____

Extra Work	Authorized By	Approx. Price

Equipment Rented Today	Rented From	Rate

Material Purchased

Supervisor's Signature _____

DAY _____   DAILY LOG   20___ DEC. 12

CONTRACTOR _____ JOB NAME _____ JOB NO _____

Work Performed Today _____

_____

_____

_____

_____

_____

_____

_____

_____

_____

_____

_____

_____

Problems - Delays _____

_____

_____

_____

Sub-Contractor Progress _____

_____

_____

_____

Special Assignments _____

_____

_____

Weather	_____
Temp. AM _____PM _____	
Safety Meeting _____	

Work Force	No.
Superintendent	_____
Clerk	_____
Bricklayers	_____
Carpenters	_____
Cement Masons	_____
Electricians	_____
Iron Workers	_____
Laborers	_____
Operating Eng.	_____
Plumbers	_____
Pipe Fitters	_____
Sheet Metal	_____
Truck Drivers	_____
Total	_____

Equipment	Hrs.

Material Purchased

Extra Work	Authorized By	Approx. Price

Equipment Rented Today	Rented From	Rate

Supervisor's Signature _____

13 DEC. 20___   DAILY LOG   DAY _____

CONTRACTOR _____ JOB NAME _____ JOB NO._____

Work Performed Today _____	Weather _____
	Temp. AM _____PM _____
	Safety Meeting _____

Work Force	No.
Superintendent	_____
Clerk	_____
Bricklayers	_____
Carpenters	_____
Cement Masons	_____
Electricians	_____
Iron Workers	_____
Laborers	_____
Operating Eng.	_____
Plumbers	_____
Pipe Fitters	_____
Sheet Metal	_____
Truck Drivers	_____
Total	_____

Problems - Delays _____

Sub-Contractor Progress _____

Equipment	Hrs.

Special Assignments _____

Material Purchased	

Extra Work	Authorized By	Approx. Price

Equipment Rented Today	Rented From	Rate

Supervisor's Signature _____

DAY _____   DAILY LOG   20___ DEC. 14

CONTRACTOR _____ JOB NAME _____ JOB NO _____

Work Performed Today _____

_____

_____

_____

_____

_____

_____

_____

_____

_____

_____

_____

_____

Problems - Delays _____

_____

_____

_____

Sub-Contractor Progress _____

_____

_____

_____

Special Assignments _____

_____

_____

_____

Weather	
Temp. AM _____ PM _____	
Safety Meeting _____	

Work Force	No.
Superintendent	_____
Clerk	_____
Bricklayers	_____
Carpenters	_____
Cement Masons	_____
Electricians	_____
Iron Workers	_____
Laborers	_____
Operating Eng.	_____
Plumbers	_____
Pipe Fitters	_____
Sheet Metal	_____
Truck Drivers	_____
Total	_____

Equipment	Hrs.

Extra Work	Authorized By	Approx. Price

Equipment Rented Today	Rented From	Rate

Material Purchased

Supervisor's Signature _____

15 DEC. 20___   DAILY LOG   DAY _____

CONTRACTOR _____ JOB NAME _____ JOB NO._____

Work Performed Today	_____

Work Performed Today _____
_____
_____
_____
_____
_____
_____
_____
_____
_____
_____
_____
_____
_____

Problems - Delays _____
_____
_____
_____
_____

Sub-Contractor Progress _____
_____
_____
_____

Special Assignments _____
_____
_____

Weather _____

Temp. AM _____PM _____

Safety Meeting _____

Work Force	No.
Superintendent	_____
Clerk	_____
Bricklayers	_____
Carpenters	_____
Cement Masons	_____
Electricians	_____
Iron Workers	_____
Laborers	_____
Operating Eng.	_____
Plumbers	_____
Pipe Fitters	_____
Sheet Metal	_____
Truck Drivers	_____
Total	_____

Equipment	Hrs.

Extra Work	Authorized By	Approx. Price

Equipment Rented Today	Rented From	Rate

Material Purchased

Supervisor's Signature _____

DAY _____   DAILY LOG   20___ DEC. 16

CONTRACTOR _____ JOB NAME _____ JOB NO _____

Work Performed Today _____

_____

_____

_____

_____

_____

_____

_____

_____

_____

_____

_____

_____

_____

Problems - Delays _____

_____

_____

_____

Sub-Contractor Progress _____

_____

_____

_____

Special Assignments _____

_____

_____

Extra Work	Authorized By	Approx. Price

Equipment Rented Today	Rented From	Rate

Supervisor's Signature _____

Weather _____

Temp. AM _____ PM _____

Safety Meeting _____

Work Force	No.
Superintendent	_____
Clerk	_____
Bricklayers	_____
Carpenters	_____
Cement Masons	_____
Electricians	_____
Iron Workers	_____
Laborers	_____
Operating Eng.	_____
Plumbers	_____
Pipe Fitters	_____
Sheet Metal	_____
Truck Drivers	_____
Total	_____

Equipment	Hrs.

Material Purchased

17 DEC. 20___   DAILY LOG   DAY _____

CONTRACTOR _____ JOB NAME _____ JOB NO._____

Work Performed Today _____

_____

_____

_____

_____

_____

_____

_____

_____

_____

_____

_____

Problems - Delays _____

_____

_____

_____

Sub-Contractor Progress _____

_____

_____

Special Assignments _____

_____

_____

Weather	_____
Temp. AM _____PM _____	

Safety Meeting _____

Work Force	No.
Superintendent	_____
Clerk	_____
Bricklayers	_____
Carpenters	_____
Cement Masons	_____
Electricians	_____
Iron Workers	_____
Laborers	_____
Operating Eng.	_____
Plumbers	_____
Pipe Fitters	_____
Sheet Metal	_____
Truck Drivers	_____
Total	_____

Equipment	Hrs.

Extra Work	Authorized By	Approx. Price

Equipment Rented Today	Rented From	Rate

Material Purchased

Supervisor's Signature _____

DAY _____   DAILY LOG   20___ DEC. 18

CONTRACTOR _____ JOB NAME _____ JOB NO _____

| Work Performed Today _____ | Weather _____ |
| _____ | Temp. AM _____PM _____ |

Safety Meeting _____

Work Force	No.
Superintendent	_____
Clerk	_____
Bricklayers	_____
Carpenters	_____
Cement Masons	_____
Electricians	_____
Iron Workers	_____
Laborers	_____
Operating Eng.	_____
Plumbers	_____
Pipe Fitters	_____
Sheet Metal	_____
Truck Drivers	_____
Total	_____

Problems - Delays _____

Sub-Contractor Progress _____

Equipment	Hrs.

Special Assignments _____

Extra Work	Authorized By	Approx. Price

Equipment Rented Today	Rented From	Rate

Material Purchased

Supervisor's Signature _____

19 DEC. 20___   DAILY LOG   DAY _____

CONTRACTOR _____ JOB NAME _____ JOB NO._____

Work Performed Today _____	Weather _____
_____	Temp. AM _____PM _____
_____	Safety Meeting _____
_____	

Work Force	No.
Superintendent	_____
Clerk	_____
Bricklayers	_____
Carpenters	_____
Cement Masons	_____
Electricians	_____
Iron Workers	_____
Laborers	_____
Operating Eng.	_____
Plumbers	_____
Pipe Fitters	_____
Sheet Metal	_____
Truck Drivers	_____
Total	_____

Problems - Delays _____
_____
_____
_____

Sub-Contractor Progress _____

Equipment	Hrs.

Special Assignments _____

Extra Work	Authorized By	Approx. Price

Equipment Rented Today	Rented From	Rate

Material Purchased

Supervisor's Signature _____

DAY _____   DAILY LOG   20___ DEC. 20

CONTRACTOR _____ JOB NAME _____ JOB NO _____

Work Performed Today _____

_____

_____

_____

_____

_____

_____

_____

_____

_____

_____

_____

_____

_____

Problems - Delays _____

_____

_____

_____

Sub-Contractor Progress _____

_____

_____

_____

Special Assignments _____

_____

_____

Extra Work	Authorized By	Approx. Price

Equipment Rented Today	Rented From	Rate

Supervisor's Signature _____

Weather _____

Temp. AM _____PM _____

Safety Meeting _____

Work Force	No.
Superintendent	_____
Clerk	_____
Bricklayers	_____
Carpenters	_____
Cement Masons	_____
Electricians	_____
Iron Workers	_____
Laborers	_____
Operating Eng.	_____
Plumbers	_____
Pipe Fitters	_____
Sheet Metal	_____
Truck Drivers	_____
Total	_____

Equipment	Hrs.

Material Purchased

21 DEC. 20___   DAILY LOG   DAY _____

CONTRACTOR _____ JOB NAME _____ JOB NO. _____

Work Performed Today _____	Weather _____
	Temp. AM _____ PM _____
	Safety Meeting _____

Work Force	No.
Superintendent	_____
Clerk	_____
Bricklayers	_____
Carpenters	_____
Cement Masons	_____
Electricians	_____
Iron Workers	_____
Laborers	_____
Operating Eng.	_____
Plumbers	_____
Pipe Fitters	_____
Sheet Metal	_____
Truck Drivers	_____
Total	_____

Problems - Delays _____

Sub-Contractor Progress _____

Equipment	Hrs.

Special Assignments _____

Extra Work	Authorized By	Approx. Price

Equipment Rented Today	Rented From	Rate

Material Purchased

Supervisor's Signature _____

DAY _____ DAILY LOG 20___ DEC. 22

CONTRACTOR _____ JOB NAME _____ JOB NO _____

Work Performed Today _____

_____

_____

_____

_____

_____

_____

_____

_____

_____

_____

_____

_____

Problems - Delays _____

_____

_____

_____

Sub-Contractor Progress _____

_____

_____

_____

Special Assignments _____

_____

_____

| Weather | _____ |
| Temp. AM _____ PM _____ |
| Safety Meeting _____ |

Work Force	No.
Superintendent	_____
Clerk	_____
Bricklayers	_____
Carpenters	_____
Cement Masons	_____
Electricians	_____
Iron Workers	_____
Laborers	_____
Operating Eng.	_____
Plumbers	_____
Pipe Fitters	_____
Sheet Metal	_____
Truck Drivers	_____
Total	_____

Equipment	Hrs.

Material Purchased	

Extra Work	Authorized By	Approx. Price

Equipment Rented Today	Rented From	Rate

Supervisor's Signature _____

23 DEC. 20___   DAILY LOG   DAY _____

CONTRACTOR _____ JOB NAME _____ JOB NO._____

Work Performed Today _____

_____

_____

_____

_____

_____

_____

_____

_____

_____

_____

_____

_____

_____

Problems - Delays _____

_____

_____

_____

Sub-Contractor Progress _____

_____

_____

_____

Special Assignments _____

_____

_____

Extra Work	Authorized By	Approx. Price

Equipment Rented Today	Rented From	Rate

Supervisor's Signature _____

Weather _____

Temp. AM _____PM _____

Safety Meeting _____

Work Force	No.
Superintendent	_____
Clerk	_____
Bricklayers	_____
Carpenters	_____
Cement Masons	_____
Electricians	_____
Iron Workers	_____
Laborers	_____
Operating Eng.	_____
Plumbers	_____
Pipe Fitters	_____
Sheet Metal	_____
Truck Drivers	_____
Total	_____

Equipment	Hrs.

Material Purchased

DAY _____   DAILY LOG   20___ DEC. 24

CONTRACTOR _____ JOB NAME _____ JOB NO _____

Work Performed Today _____	Weather _____
_____	Temp. AM _____ PM _____
_____	Safety Meeting _____
_____	

Work Force	No.
Superintendent	_____
Clerk	_____
Bricklayers	_____
Carpenters	_____
Cement Masons	_____
Electricians	_____
Iron Workers	_____
Laborers	_____
Operating Eng.	_____
Plumbers	_____
Pipe Fitters	_____
Sheet Metal	_____
Truck Drivers	_____
Total	_____

Problems - Delays _____
_____
_____
_____

Sub-Contractor Progress _____
_____
_____
_____

Equipment	Hrs.

Special Assignments _____
_____
_____

Extra Work	Authorized By	Approx. Price

Equipment Rented Today	Rented From	Rate

Material Purchased

Supervisor's Signature _____

25 DEC. 20___   DAILY LOG   DAY _____

CONTRACTOR _____ JOB NAME _____ JOB NO._____

Work Performed Today _____	Weather_____
_____	Temp. AM _____PM _____
_____	Safety Meeting _____

Work Force	No.
Superintendent	_____
Clerk	_____
Bricklayers	_____
Carpenters	_____
Cement Masons	_____
Electricians	_____
Iron Workers	_____
Laborers	_____
Operating Eng.	_____
Plumbers	_____
Pipe Fitters	_____
Sheet Metal	_____
Truck Drivers	_____
Total	_____

Problems - Delays _____

Sub-Contractor Progress _____

Equipment	Hrs.

Special Assignments _____

Extra Work	Authorized By	Approx. Price

Material Purchased

Equipment Rented Today	Rented From	Rate

Supervisor's Signature _____

DAY _____   DAILY LOG   20___ DEC. 26

CONTRACTOR _____ JOB NAME _____ JOB NO _____

Work Performed Today _____	Weather _____
	Temp. AM _____ PM _____
	Safety Meeting _____

Work Force	No.
Superintendent	_____
Clerk	_____
Bricklayers	_____
Carpenters	_____
Cement Masons	_____
Electricians	_____
Iron Workers	_____
Laborers	_____
Operating Eng.	_____
Plumbers	_____
Pipe Fitters	_____
Sheet Metal	_____
Truck Drivers	_____
Total	_____

Problems - Delays _____

Equipment	Hrs.

Sub-Contractor Progress _____

Special Assignments _____

Extra Work	Authorized By	Approx. Price

Equipment Rented Today	Rented From	Rate

Material Purchased

Supervisor's Signature _____

27 DEC. 20___   DAILY LOG   DAY _____

CONTRACTOR _____ JOB NAME _____ JOB NO._____

Work Performed Today _____	Weather _____
_____	Temp. AM _____PM _____
_____	Safety Meeting _____

Work Force	No.
Superintendent	_____
Clerk	_____
Bricklayers	_____
Carpenters	_____
Cement Masons	_____
Electricians	_____
Iron Workers	_____
Laborers	_____
Operating Eng.	_____
Plumbers	_____
Pipe Fitters	_____
Sheet Metal	_____
Truck Drivers	_____
Total	_____

Work Performed Today _____

_____

_____

_____

_____

_____

_____

_____

_____

_____

_____

Problems - Delays _____

_____

_____

_____

Sub-Contractor Progress _____

_____

_____

_____

Special Assignments _____

_____

_____

Equipment	Hrs.

Extra Work	Authorized By	Approx. Price

Equipment Rented Today	Rented From	Rate

Material Purchased

Supervisor's Signature _____

DAY _____   DAILY LOG   20___ DEC. 28

CONTRACTOR _____ JOB NAME _____ JOB NO _____

Work Performed Today _____

_____

_____

_____

_____

_____

_____

_____

_____

_____

_____

_____

_____

_____

Problems - Delays _____

_____

_____

_____

Sub-Contractor Progress _____

_____

_____

_____

Special Assignments _____

_____

_____

_____

Weather	_____
Temp. AM _____ PM _____	

Safety Meeting _____

Work Force	No.
Superintendent	_____
Clerk	_____
Bricklayers	_____
Carpenters	_____
Cement Masons	_____
Electricians	_____
Iron Workers	_____
Laborers	_____
Operating Eng.	_____
Plumbers	_____
Pipe Fitters	_____
Sheet Metal	_____
Truck Drivers	_____
Total	_____

Equipment	Hrs.

Material Purchased

Extra Work	Authorized By	Approx. Price

Equipment Rented Today	Rented From	Rate

Supervisor's Signature _____

29 DEC. 20___   DAILY LOG   DAY _____

CONTRACTOR _____ JOB NAME _____ JOB NO._____

Work Performed Today		Weather _____

Work Performed Today _____

Weather _____

Temp. AM _____ PM _____

Safety Meeting _____

Work Force	No.
Superintendent	_____
Clerk	_____
Bricklayers	_____
Carpenters	_____
Cement Masons	_____
Electricians	_____
Iron Workers	_____
Laborers	_____
Operating Eng.	_____
Plumbers	_____
Pipe Fitters	_____
Sheet Metal	_____
Truck Drivers	_____
Total	_____

Problems - Delays _____

Equipment	Hrs.

Sub-Contractor Progress _____

Special Assignments _____

Material Purchased

Extra Work	Authorized By	Approx. Price

Equipment Rented Today	Rented From	Rate

Supervisor's Signature _____

DAY _____   DAILY LOG   20___ DEC. 30

CONTRACTOR _____ JOB NAME _____ JOB NO _____

Work Performed Today _____

_____

_____

_____

_____

_____

_____

_____

_____

_____

_____

_____

_____

Problems - Delays _____

_____

_____

_____

Sub-Contractor Progress _____

_____

_____

_____

Special Assignments _____

_____

_____

Extra Work	Authorized By	Approx. Price

Equipment Rented Today	Rented From	Rate

Supervisor's Signature _____

Weather _____

Temp. AM _____ PM _____

Safety Meeting _____

Work Force	No.
Superintendent	_____
Clerk	_____
Bricklayers	_____
Carpenters	_____
Cement Masons	_____
Electricians	_____
Iron Workers	_____
Laborers	_____
Operating Eng.	_____
Plumbers	_____
Pipe Fitters	_____
Sheet Metal	_____
Truck Drivers	_____
Total	_____

Equipment	Hrs.

Material Purchased

31 DEC. 20____   DAILY LOG   DAY _____

CONTRACTOR _____ JOB NAME _____ JOB NO._____

Work Performed Today _____	Weather _____
	Temp. AM _____ PM _____
	Safety Meeting _____

Work Force	No.
Superintendent	_____
Clerk	_____
Bricklayers	_____
Carpenters	_____
Cement Masons	_____
Electricians	_____
Iron Workers	_____
Laborers	_____
Operating Eng.	_____
Plumbers	_____
Pipe Fitters	_____
Sheet Metal	_____
Truck Drivers	_____
Total	_____

Problems - Delays _____

Equipment	Hrs.

Sub-Contractor Progress _____

Special Assignments _____

Extra Work	Authorized By	Approx. Price

Equipment Rented Today	Rented From	Rate

Material Purchased

Supervisor's Signature _____

ACCIDENT REPORT

DAY _____ DATE_____ TIME OF ACCIDENT_____

CONTRACTOR_____ JOB NAME _____ JOB NO. _____

NAME OF INJURED _____ AGE _____ SEX _____

ADDRESS_____ OCCUPATION_____

TYPE OF INJURY _____

HOW AND WHERE IT HAPPENED _____

_____

_____

WHAT WAS INJURED PERSON DOING WHEN ACCIDENT OCCURED?_____

_____

WHO ADMINISTERED FIRST AID? _____

DESCRIBE FIRST AID TREATMENT _____

_____

TIME AMBULANCE ARRIVED _____ NAME OF AMBULANCE SERV. _____

NAME OF HOSPITAL_____ NAME OF DOCTOR _____

WILL THIS BE A LOSS TIME ACCIDENT?_____ HOW LONG?_____

WAS STATEMENT TAKEN FROM INJURED? _____ FROM WITNESS? _____

DESCRIBE ACCIDENT SCENE IN DETAIL_____

_____

_____

WAS ACTION TAKEN TO PREVENT RECURRENCE? _____

WITNESSES _____   _____

_____   _____

_____   _____

ATTACH COPIES OF ANY PHOTOGRAPHS OF ACCIDENT SCENE TO THIS SHEET _____

FEDERAL & STATE REPORTS FILED.   YES _____ NO _____ N/A_____

SUPERVISOR'S SIGNATURE _____

ACCIDENT REPORT

DAY _____ DATE_____ TIME OF ACCIDENT_____

CONTRACTOR_____ JOB NAME _____ JOB NO. _____

NAME OF INJURED _____ AGE _____ SEX _____

ADDRESS_____ OCCUPATION _____

TYPE OF INJURY _____

HOW AND WHERE IT HAPPENED _____

_____

_____

WHAT WAS INJURED PERSON DOING WHEN ACCIDENT OCCURED?_____

_____

WHO ADMINISTERED FIRST AID?_____

DESCRIBE FIRST AID TREATMENT _____

_____

TIME AMBULANCE ARRIVED _____ NAME OF AMBULANCE SERV. _____

NAME OF HOSPITAL _____ NAME OF DOCTOR _____

WILL THIS BE A LOSS TIME ACCIDENT?_____ HOW LONG?_____

WAS STATEMENT TAKEN FROM INJURED? _____ FROM WITNESS? _____

DESCRIBE ACCIDENT SCENE IN DETAIL_____

_____

_____

WAS ACTION TAKEN TO PREVENT RECURRENCE? _____

WITNESSES _____   _____

_____   _____

_____   _____

ATTACH COPIES OF ANY PHOTOGRAPHS OF ACCIDENT SCENE TO THIS SHEET _____

FEDERAL & STATE REPORTS FILED.   YES _____ NO _____ N/A_____

SUPERVISOR'S SIGNATURE _____

ACCIDENT REPORT

DAY _____ DATE_____ TIME OF ACCIDENT_____

CONTRACTOR_____ JOB NAME _____ JOB NO. _____

NAME OF INJURED _____ AGE _____ SEX _____

ADDRESS_____ OCCUPATION_____

TYPE OF INJURY _____

HOW AND WHERE IT HAPPENED _____

_____

_____

WHAT WAS INJURED PERSON DOING WHEN ACCIDENT OCCURED?_____

_____

WHO ADMINISTERED FIRST AID? _____

DESCRIBE FIRST AID TREATMENT _____

_____

TIME AMBULANCE ARRIVED _____ NAME OF AMBULANCE SERV. _____

NAME OF HOSPITAL_____ NAME OF DOCTOR _____

WILL THIS BE A LOSS TIME ACCIDENT?_____ HOW LONG?_____

WAS STATEMENT TAKEN FROM INJURED? _____ FROM WITNESS? _____

DESCRIBE ACCIDENT SCENE IN DETAIL_____

_____

_____

WAS ACTION TAKEN TO PREVENT RECURRENCE? _____

WITNESSES _____ _____

_____ _____

_____ _____

ATTACH COPIES OF ANY PHOTOGRAPHS OF ACCIDENT SCENE TO THIS SHEET _____

FEDERAL & STATE REPORTS FILED. YES _____ NO _____ N/A_____

SUPERVISOR'S SIGNATURE _____

ACCIDENT REPORT

DAY _____ DATE_____ TIME OF ACCIDENT_____

CONTRACTOR_____ JOB NAME _____ JOB NO. _____

NAME OF INJURED _____ AGE _____ SEX _____

ADDRESS _____ OCCUPATION _____

TYPE OF INJURY _____

HOW AND WHERE IT HAPPENED _____

_____

_____

WHAT WAS INJURED PERSON DOING WHEN ACCIDENT OCCURED?_____

_____

WHO ADMINISTERED FIRST AID? _____

DESCRIBE FIRST AID TREATMENT _____

_____

TIME AMBULANCE ARRIVED _____ NAME OF AMBULANCE SERV. _____

NAME OF HOSPITAL_____ NAME OF DOCTOR _____

WILL THIS BE A LOSS TIME ACCIDENT?_____ HOW LONG?_____

WAS STATEMENT TAKEN FROM INJURED? _____ FROM WITNESS? _____

DESCRIBE ACCIDENT SCENE IN DETAIL_____

_____

_____

WAS ACTION TAKEN TO PREVENT RECURRENCE? _____

WITNESSES _____   _____

_____   _____

_____   _____

ATTACH COPIES OF ANY PHOTOGRAPHS OF ACCIDENT SCENE TO THIS SHEET _____

FEDERAL & STATE REPORTS FILED.   YES _____ NO _____ N/A_____

SUPERVISOR'S SIGNATURE _____

ACCIDENT REPORT

DAY _____ DATE_____ TIME OF ACCIDENT_____

CONTRACTOR_____ JOB NAME _____ JOB NO. _____

NAME OF INJURED _____ AGE _____ SEX _____

ADDRESS_____ OCCUPATION_____

TYPE OF INJURY _____

HOW AND WHERE IT HAPPENED _____

_____

_____

WHAT WAS INJURED PERSON DOING WHEN ACCIDENT OCCURED?_____

_____

WHO ADMINISTERED FIRST AID?_____

DESCRIBE FIRST AID TREATMENT _____

_____

TIME AMBULANCE ARRIVED _____ NAME OF AMBULANCE SERV. _____

NAME OF HOSPITAL_____ NAME OF DOCTOR _____

WILL THIS BE A LOSS TIME ACCIDENT?_____ HOW LONG?_____

WAS STATEMENT TAKEN FROM INJURED? _____ FROM WITNESS? _____

DESCRIBE ACCIDENT SCENE IN DETAIL_____

_____

_____

WAS ACTION TAKEN TO PREVENT RECURRENCE? _____

WITNESSES _____ _____

_____ _____

_____ _____

ATTACH COPIES OF ANY PHOTOGRAPHS OF ACCIDENT SCENE TO THIS SHEET _____

FEDERAL & STATE REPORTS FILED.   YES _____ NO _____ N/A_____

SUPERVISOR'S SIGNATURE _____

ACCIDENT REPORT

DAY _____ DATE_____ TIME OF ACCIDENT_____

CONTRACTOR_____ JOB NAME _____ JOB NO. _____

NAME OF INJURED _____ AGE _____ SEX _____

ADDRESS_____ OCCUPATION_____

TYPE OF INJURY _____

HOW AND WHERE IT HAPPENED _____

_____

_____

WHAT WAS INJURED PERSON DOING WHEN ACCIDENT OCCURED?_____

_____

WHO ADMINISTERED FIRST AID? _____

DESCRIBE FIRST AID TREATMENT _____

_____

TIME AMBULANCE ARRIVED _____ NAME OF AMBULANCE SERV. ___

NAME OF HOSPITAL_____ NAME OF DOCTOR _____

WILL THIS BE A LOSS TIME ACCIDENT?_____ HOW LONG?_____

WAS STATEMENT TAKEN FROM INJURED? _____ FROM WITNESS? _____

DESCRIBE ACCIDENT SCENE IN DETAIL_____

_____

_____

WAS ACTION TAKEN TO PREVENT RECURRENCE? _____

WITNESSES _____   _____

                    _____   _____

                    _____   _____

ATTACH COPIES OF ANY PHOTOGRAPHS OF ACCIDENT SCENE TO THIS SHEET _____

FEDERAL & STATE REPORTS FILED.   YES _____ NO _____ N/A_____

SUPERVISOR'S SIGNATURE _____

ACCIDENT REPORT

DAY _____ DATE_____ TIME OF ACCIDENT_____

CONTRACTOR_____ JOB NAME _____ JOB NO. _____

NAME OF INJURED _____ AGE _____ SEX _____

ADDRESS_____ OCCUPATION_____

TYPE OF INJURY _____

HOW AND WHERE IT HAPPENED _____

_____

_____

WHAT WAS INJURED PERSON DOING WHEN ACCIDENT OCCURED?_____

_____

WHO ADMINISTERED FIRST AID? _____

DESCRIBE FIRST AID TREATMENT _____

_____

TIME AMBULANCE ARRIVED _____ NAME OF AMBULANCE SERV. _____

NAME OF HOSPITAL_____ NAME OF DOCTOR _____

WILL THIS BE A LOSS TIME ACCIDENT?_____ HOW LONG?_____

WAS STATEMENT TAKEN FROM INJURED? _____ FROM WITNESS? _____

DESCRIBE ACCIDENT SCENE IN DETAIL_____

_____

_____

WAS ACTION TAKEN TO PREVENT RECURRENCE? _____

WITNESSES _____   _____

_____   _____

_____   _____

ATTACH COPIES OF ANY PHOTOGRAPHS OF ACCIDENT SCENE TO THIS SHEET _____

FEDERAL & STATE REPORTS FILED.   YES _____ NO _____ N/A_____

SUPERVISOR'S SIGNATURE _____

ACCIDENT REPORT

DAY _____ DATE_____ TIME OF ACCIDENT_____

CONTRACTOR_____ JOB NAME _____ JOB NO. _____

NAME OF INJURED _____ AGE _____ SEX _____

ADDRESS _____ OCCUPATION _____

TYPE OF INJURY _____

HOW AND WHERE IT HAPPENED _____

_____

_____

WHAT WAS INJURED PERSON DOING WHEN ACCIDENT OCCURED? _____

_____

WHO ADMINISTERED FIRST AID? _____

DESCRIBE FIRST AID TREATMENT _____

_____

TIME AMBULANCE ARRIVED _____ NAME OF AMBULANCE SERV. _____

NAME OF HOSPITAL_____ NAME OF DOCTOR _____

WILL THIS BE A LOSS TIME ACCIDENT?_____ HOW LONG?_____

WAS STATEMENT TAKEN FROM INJURED? _____ FROM WITNESS? _____

DESCRIBE ACCIDENT SCENE IN DETAIL_____

_____

_____

WAS ACTION TAKEN TO PREVENT RECURRENCE? _____

WITNESSES _____   _____

_____   _____

_____   _____

ATTACH COPIES OF ANY PHOTOGRAPHS OF ACCIDENT SCENE TO THIS SHEET _____

FEDERAL & STATE REPORTS FILED.   YES _____ NO _____ N/A_____

SUPERVISOR'S SIGNATURE _____

ACCIDENT REPORT

DAY _____ DATE_____ TIME OF ACCIDENT_____

CONTRACTOR_____ JOB NAME _____ JOB NO. _____

NAME OF INJURED _____ AGE _____ SEX _____

ADDRESS_____ OCCUPATION_____

TYPE OF INJURY _____

HOW AND WHERE IT HAPPENED _____

_____

_____

WHAT WAS INJURED PERSON DOING WHEN ACCIDENT OCCURED?_____

_____

WHO ADMINISTERED FIRST AID? _____

DESCRIBE FIRST AID TREATMENT _____

_____

TIME AMBULANCE ARRIVED _____ NAME OF AMBULANCE SERV. _____

NAME OF HOSPITAL_____ NAME OF DOCTOR _____

WILL THIS BE A LOSS TIME ACCIDENT?_____ HOW LONG?_____

WAS STATEMENT TAKEN FROM INJURED? _____ FROM WITNESS? _____

DESCRIBE ACCIDENT SCENE IN DETAIL_____

_____

_____

WAS ACTION TAKEN TO PREVENT RECURRENCE? _____

WITNESSES _____   _____

_____   _____

_____   _____

ATTACH COPIES OF ANY PHOTOGRAPHS OF ACCIDENT SCENE TO THIS SHEET _____

FEDERAL & STATE REPORTS FILED.   YES _____ NO _____ N/A_____

SUPERVISOR'S SIGNATURE _____

NOTES

NOTES

NOTES

NOTES

NOTES

2018

JANUARY
S	M	T	W	T	F	S
	1	2	3	4	5	6
7	8	9	10	11	12	13
14	15	16	17	18	19	20
21	22	23	24	25	26	27
28	29	30	31			

FEBRUARY
S	M	T	W	T	F	S
				1	2	3
4	5	6	7	8	9	10
11	12	13	14	15	16	17
18	19	20	21	22	23	24
25	26	27	28			

MARCH
S	M	T	W	T	F	S
				1	2	3
4	5	6	7	8	9	10
11	12	13	14	15	16	17
18	19	20	21	22	23	24
25	26	27	28	29	30	31

APRIL
S	M	T	W	T	F	S
1	2	3	4	5	6	7
8	9	10	11	12	13	14
15	16	17	18	19	20	21
22	23	24	25	26	27	28
29	30					

MAY
S	M	T	W	T	F	S
		1	2	3	4	5
6	7	8	9	10	11	12
13	14	15	16	17	18	19
20	21	22	23	24	25	26
27	28	29	30	31		

JUNE
S	M	T	W	T	F	S
					1	2
3	4	5	6	7	8	9
10	11	12	13	14	15	16
17	18	19	20	21	22	23
24	25	26	27	28	29	30

JULY
S	M	T	W	T	F	S
1	2	3	4	5	6	7
8	9	10	11	12	13	14
15	16	17	18	19	20	21
22	23	24	25	26	27	28
29	30	31				

AUGUST
S	M	T	W	T	F	S
			1	2	3	4
5	6	7	8	9	10	11
12	13	14	15	16	17	18
19	20	21	22	23	24	25
26	27	28	29	30	31	

SEPTEMBER
S	M	T	W	T	F	S
						1
2	3	4	5	6	7	8
9	10	11	12	13	14	15
16	17	18	19	20	21	22
23	24	25	26	27	28	29
30						

OCTOBER
S	M	T	W	T	F	S
	1	2	3	4	5	6
7	8	9	10	11	12	13
14	15	16	17	18	19	20
21	22	23	24	25	26	27
28	29	30	31			

NOVEMBER
S	M	T	W	T	F	S
				1	2	3
4	5	6	7	8	9	10
11	12	13	14	15	16	17
18	19	20	21	22	23	24
25	26	27	28	29	30	

DECEMBER
S	M	T	W	T	F	S
						1
2	3	4	5	6	7	8
9	10	11	12	13	14	15
16	17	18	19	20	21	22
23	24	25	26	27	28	29
30	31					

2019

JANUARY
S	M	T	W	T	F	S
		1	2	3	4	5
6	7	8	9	10	11	12
13	14	15	16	17	18	19
20	21	22	23	24	25	26
27	28	29	30	31		

FEBRUARY
S	M	T	W	T	F	S
					1	2
3	4	5	6	7	8	9
10	11	12	13	14	15	16
17	18	19	20	21	22	23
24	25	26	27	28		

MARCH
S	M	T	W	T	F	S
					1	2
3	4	5	6	7	8	9
10	11	12	13	14	15	16
17	18	19	20	21	22	23
24	25	26	27	28	29	30
31						

APRIL
S	M	T	W	T	F	S
	1	2	3	4	5	6
7	8	9	10	11	12	13
14	15	16	17	18	19	20
21	22	23	24	25	26	27
28	29	30				

MAY
S	M	T	W	T	F	S
			1	2	3	4
5	6	7	8	9	10	11
12	13	14	15	16	17	18
19	20	21	22	23	24	25
26	27	28	29	30	31	

JUNE
S	M	T	W	T	F	S
						1
2	3	4	5	6	7	8
9	10	11	12	13	14	15
16	17	18	19	20	21	22
23	24	25	26	27	28	29
30						

JULY
S	M	T	W	T	F	S
	1	2	3	4	5	6
7	8	9	10	11	12	13
14	15	16	17	18	19	20
21	22	23	24	25	26	27
28	29	30	31			

AUGUST
S	M	T	W	T	F	S
				1	2	3
4	5	6	7	8	9	10
11	12	13	14	15	16	17
18	19	20	21	22	23	24
25	26	27	28	29	30	31

SEPTEMBER
S	M	T	W	T	F	S
1	2	3	4	5	6	7
8	9	10	11	12	13	14
15	16	17	18	19	20	21
22	23	24	25	26	27	28
29	30					

OCTOBER
S	M	T	W	T	F	S
		1	2	3	4	5
6	7	8	9	10	11	12
13	14	15	16	17	18	19
20	21	22	23	24	25	26
27	28	29	30	31		

NOVEMBER
S	M	T	W	T	F	S
					1	2
3	4	5	6	7	8	9
10	11	12	13	14	15	16
17	18	19	20	21	22	23
24	25	26	27	28	29	30

DECEMBER
S	M	T	W	T	F	S
1	2	3	4	5	6	7
8	9	10	11	12	13	14
15	16	17	18	19	20	21
22	23	24	25	26	27	28
29	30	31				